the Forth
Naturalist

Historian

Volume 5, 1980

CONTENTS

3 Why the Border Shook on Boxing Day, Iain Bain

7 Annual Climatological Bulletin 1980, S. J. Harrison

23 Rainfall in the Stirling Area, S. J. Harrison

35 Fish Entrained in 1977 at Cockenzie Power Station, in the Firth of Forth, Peter S. Maitland, Kenneth East and Kenneth H. Morris

46 Forth Area Bird Report (Clacks, Stirling, Southwest Perth) 1980, C. J. Henty

67 Nocturnal Migration in Southwest and Central Scotland Detected by Moonwatching, C. J. Henty

72 The True Bugs (Heteroptera) of Tentsmuir Point, Fife, James K. Campbell

87 Ashfield — a Factory Village in South Perthshire, John D. Williams

96 Education in Bothkennar Parish in the Time of the Rev. William Nimmo, Historian of Stirlingshire, Andrew Bain

107 Some Background Notes on William Nimmo (1733-1788), First Historian of Stirlingshire, William B. Maclaren and Andrew Bain

114 The Old Scottish Poor Law — the Practice of Stirlingshire 1790-1845, D. E. Gladstone

130 Authors Addresses

2 Published by the Editorial Board, University of Stirling and the Central Regional Council, Stirling, 1982

ISSN 0309-7560

Cover produced and donated by the BP Group of Companies in Scotland.

Cover illustrations from photography by E. Blake.

Front: Adult male Hen Harrier and young

Back: Adult female and juvenile with eggs

WHY THE BORDER SHOOK ON BOXING DAY   3

Iain Bain
Geographical Magazine

The British Isles are popularly believed to be located in a stable part of the world, free from disastrous earthquakes. But earth tremors, some of them large, do occur and usually take the British by surprise. Iain Bain examines some of the possible causes of the earthquake which occurred under the small Cumbrian town of Longtown last Boxing Day.

In the British context the earthquake which shook southern Scotland and part of northern England out of its Boxing Day torpor last year was a considerable seismic event. The earthquake measured 5.2 on the Richter scale of magnitude which makes it possibly the largest earthquake felt in Britain since the famous Colchester earthquake (5.25 Richter) in 1885. As a media topic, the shock of the Boxing Day earthquake rapidly died away, eclipsed by events elsewhere. Scientific interest remains strong, however, and it seems that this particular tremor will be the most intensively studied of all British earthquakes.

Perhaps part of the reason for the loss of Press interest was that immediately after the announcement of the basic seismic facts, where and how strong, the experts were unable to offer much more information. This is because although seismic information is recorded instantaneously the data are complex and require lengthy and detailed analysis. Results are beginning to come through now which allow some speculation on the causes of the 'quake.

Scientists at the Global Seismology Unit of the Institute of Geological Sciences in Edinburgh were able to locate the earthquake rapidly using the Lownet network of seismometers. This network comprises seven instruments sited in Central and Southern Scotland, from Dundee to Broad Law in the Southern Uplands, which are linked by radio to a central station in Edinburgh. Earthquake shocks produce a number of different vibrations and the determination of an earthquake epicentre concentrates on the high frequency end of the spectrum. Epicentres are located by measuring delays between the arrival at different stations of P-waves (longitudinal waves which pass through the liquid part of the earth's core) and S-waves (transverse waves which travel only through the earth's crust). In the case of the Boxing Day earthquake the epicentre was located at $55.01^{o}N$, $2.97^{o}W$ at a depth of eleven kilometres. This puts it almost

4 immediately under the village of Longtown in Cumbria just south of the Scottish Border.

Seismic activity is not unknown in this part of the Border. From October to December 1979 the Global Seismology Unit detected four tremors in the Longtown-Gretna area at a depth of two kilometres. Following the Boxing Day earthquake twenty-two shocks were recorded by the GSU up to January 8; most were small but one, on New Year's Day, measured 4.1 on the Richter Scale, in almost the same place as the Boxing Day quake but at only three kilometres depth. A survey of the impact of the Boxing Day earthquake on the people within the area in which it was felt is being carried out by the GSU. A questionnaire form was published in a national newspaper soon after the event and between 3000 and 4000 replies have been received by the GSU. Results will be analysed later this year.

Intensive recording and analysis of the after shocks which follow a large earthquake can tell seismologists a good deal about the character of the initial event and for the first time for a British earthquake this was done at Longtown. A team of geophysicists from the University of Cambridge under Dr Geoff King began setting up a network of eight portable recorders in the locality on December 26 and began recording the next day until January 2. Twenty-seven earthquakes were detected during this period and locations were obtained for twenty-two of them. The Cambridge team put the centre of the aftershock region five kilometres east of Longtown, results which compare in general with those of the GSU. The fault plane solution which they obtained suggested a mechanism for the earthquake and it is believed that the motion is a thrust along a strike aligned east-west and dipping either 35° to the north or 55° to the south. It is suggested that the displacement is about thirty centimetres occurring over an area of nine square kilometres.

In a populated country the possibility of seismic risk is a worrying one, the more so in this area where a nuclear power station is sited not very far away at Chapelcross near Annan. The question, why an earthquake occurred at Longtown, is one to which the answer must remain speculative at the moment. However, the geological background does contain some indications.

Longtown's geological basis is sedimentary, the result of the steady infilling of the Solway Basin, one of the most enduring of Britain's major landforms. At the surface Triassic deposits cover Carboniferous sediments and at depth the area is underlain by the same highly deformed rocks which form the Southern Uplands, Lakeland hills and much of Wales. The Solway also has a considerable tectonic pedigree. In the Cambrian and Ordivician eras (570,000,000 to 445,000,000 years ago) the area which is now the British Isles was divided and the two halves, effectively North and South Britain, lay on separate tectonic plates on either side of a deep proto-Atlantic sea which geologists have termed the Iapetus Ocean. Gradually the process of continental drift narrowed the Iapetus Ocean and it finally closed in the late Silurian era, about 400,000,000 years ago. It has been suggested that the collision line between the two continental masses, termed the 'Iapetus Suture', runs up the Solway, passes through the head of the Firth and follows roughly the line of the Border. The actual existence of the Iapetus Suture has been a matter of speculation for some time but it is only recently in the late 1970s that aeromagnetic surveys have indicated a juxtaposition of magentic anomaly patterns in the Solway area which point to a possible location for the suture.

It would be tempting indeed to think that this ancient collision has resulted in a line of weakness which promoted the seismic events earlier this year. The problem is one of establishing a convincing link between the two. One clue may lie in concealed faulting in the Longtown area. To the north of Longtown lies the small and now defunct Canonbie coalfield. In general, the coal measures in this area have been eroded from the upper part of the Carboniferous sediments but the Canonbie coalfield exists because it has been let down between a pair of deep faults six kilometres apart. A downward displacement of a few hundred metres has allowed the coal measures to be preserved. The coalfield and the faults are marked by the cover of Triassic deposits.

The village of Longtown lies over the concealed southern boundary fault of the Canonbie coalfield and coincidence of this and the majority of the locations obtained by the seismologists makes movement here a likely explanation for the earthquake. And, possibly, the Canonbie faults may be related to the earlier Iapetus Suture. One problem which still exists is that the Cambridge geophysicists' results point to a thrust along a much shallower angle than the near vertical lines which the Canonbie faults are assumed to take. The answer to this may lie in a reassessment of the dip of the faults. No-one is really sure what happens to faults at depth and it has been suggested by some geologists that they may flatten out to give shallower angles of dip.

Commenting on the suggested dip angle of $35^{\circ}N/55^{\circ}S$ Fred Dunning of the Geological Museum pointed out that this could relate to the collision of plates in the late Silurian era and the way in which sediments were compressed, distorted and buried under the leading edges of plates. He said that: 'There are numerous fracture structures in the Southern Uplands dipping at 35° north which are part of a postulated accretionary prism structure and the Iapetus Suture itself

6 may follow the same line of weakness as one of these flat north-dipping structures'. If the dip was 55° south then he thought the shock was more likely to be caused by movement on the coalfield boundary faults.

Consideration of the geological background provides knowledge of why earthquakes occur where they do. What actually causes an earthquake to occur when it does is another matter. In the case of the Longtown earthquake there is a general consensus that the trigger was possible post-glacial isostatic uplift. The weight of glacial ice, particularly in Scotland, caused a depression of the earth's crust and a consequent rebounding of the land when relieved of weight. The stress set up by that readjustment, small in Cumbria since it is relatively far from the main centre of isostatic uplift in the south-west Highlands, may have been sufficient to set off the Longtown earthquake.

EDITORIAL NOTE

Since this Boxing Day earthquake was felt by many of our readers in Stirling and the Hillfoots and is therefore of particular interest, we are grateful to Iain Bain for permission to reprint this article from the *Geographical Magazine* of April 1980. As indicated in our note at the end of the Burton and Neilson paper *Earthquake Swarms in Scotland* in our last issue, we did expect an IGS paper on this subject, but since then the new Head of IGS's Gobal Seismology Unit (Dr Browitt) has been unwilling to allow us such a paper.

For local newspaper notes see: *Glasgow Herald* 28th December, 1979 and 3rd January, 1980, and *Stirling Observer* 26th December, 1979; and on the October 1980 tremor felt by readers in Alva *Alloa Advertiser* 29th October, 1980.

ANNUAL CLIMATOLOGICAL BULLETIN No. 2 1980   7

S. J. Harrison
University of Stirling

This year's bulletin makes reference to observations from two climatological stations: Parkhead on Stirling University campus, and Carim in the Ochil Hills.

Stirling (Parkhead)
Grid Reference: NS 815969
Height above sea-level: 35 metres
    The station is located in the University glasshouse area at the eastern end of the campus. Monthly returns of daily observations are submitted to the Meteorological Office in Edinburgh by Mr Liddell, of the University's Department of Biology. Observations include

(i) Air temperature: Daily maximum
                      Daily minimum
                      Dry bulb
                      Wet bulb
(ii) Soil temperature at 30 cm
(iii) Total rainfall
and also wind speed and direction, visibility and state of ground. .

Ochil Hills (Carim)
Grid Reference: NN 864049
Height above sea-level: 332 m
    The Department of Environmental Science is currently developing research and teaching in upland environments and has established an experimental site in the Ochil Hills, in the upper catchment of the Burn of Ogilvie, near to the ruined Carim Lodge. During 1980 streamflow monitoring equipment and a climatological station have been installed. The latter was completed in January and began to produce reliable observations in April. Because of the remoteness of the site weather recording is automatic.
    Air temperature is monitored using a bimetallic thermograph, and relative humidity using a hair hygrograph. Both are located in a large thermometer screen and have their sensors about 1.2 m above the ground surface. Rainfall is recorded using a tipping-bucket raingauge which registers in increments of 0.5 mm. A run-of-wind anemometer provides a value of mean wind speed over a fixed time interval.
    The Royal Meteorological Society have also loaned several small raingauges one of which has been installed as a ground-level gauge,

8 surrounded by a 1-m^2 anti-splash grid.

The site is visited on Mondays when charts are changed on the instruments. Checks are made against standards at the beginning and end of each week. Daily maximum and minimum air temperature and precipitation are extracted from the charts and summary tables prepared at the end of each month.

The Weather of 1980

1980 may well go down in the record books as the year of the false starts as far as the weather is concerned. A very mild spell in February promised us an early Spring and the dry warm weather of April and May raised hopes of a good summer but neither materialised. Summer, as in 1979, was dominated by cloud and rain, and warm sunny days were very rare in Scotland. At the end of the year we came close to having a White Christmas.

January. Cool but relatively dry.

Pressure remained high over Scotland during the New Year holiday and the weather was calm and clear. Air temperatures remained low and this was the coldest spell of the month. Milder weather followed on the 3rd with heavy rain and relatively strong westerly winds. The return of anticyclonic conditions on the 10th brought some mist and low overnight temperatures, but no air frosts. A cold front moving south on the 13th and 14th brought snow to many parts. Temperatures remained low, the daytime maximum at Parkhead reaching only 2.0°C on the 17th. More unsettled weather returned on the 19th as a cold front moved eastwards across Britain. On the 21st, an extremely vigorous depression brought gales and heavy rain. As the depression stagnated over Scotland and the strong winds subsided there was a brief mild interlude. A ridge of high pressure extending south-eastwards from Iceland on the 25th saw a return to calm cool weather until the 28th when unsettled Atlantic weather returned, with rain. By the end of the month winds had freshened from the north-east with the promise of snow.

February. Cold at first but becoming exceptionally mild.

The first few days brought strong north-easterly winds and heavy snow. Blizzard conditions were reported in many parts of Scotland. Daytime temperatures failed to rise above 2°C for 3 days. This was in sharp contrast to southern England where temperatures were well above the seasonal normal. The snow lingered over the weekend and was still lying on Monday 4th. Winds were fresh to strong westerlies. Mild and muggy conditions with winds mainly from a south-westerly quarter dominated the weather for the next two weeks. Air temperatures were particularly high during the day reaching an **9** unseasonal 11°C at Parkhead on the 14th. Night frosts were notably absent, temperatures falling to only 6.5°C on the 13th. This false Spring brought many trees and shrubs into early bud. Rainfall was recorded on most days during this period and was particularly persistent on the 9th and 12th. Pressure rose gradually after the 22nd and for much of the remainder of the month the weather became more settled. Cloudy skies limited nocturnal cooling and slight air frosts were recorded on only three evenings.

March. A cool wet month.

Temperatures fell gradually over the first few days as high pressure to the west of the country brought northerly air across Scotland. Night-time temperatures fell to −3.7°C on the 3rd. This cold period was replaced by one of unsettled Atlantic weather on the 4th bringing milder conditions to Scotland until the 13th. As a ridge of high pressure developed over northern Europe an easterly airstream was established. Daytime temperatures reached only 3.5°C on the 18th when winds were in excess of 27 mph. The easterly winds waned after the 20th but on the 21st a slow-moving front brought heavy snowfall to much of Scotland. Temperatures fell to below −4.0°C on four consecutive nights, from the 21st to the 24th. Low pressure dominated the weather picture for the remainder of the month. Daytime temperatures recovered sharply to reach 10°C on the 25th, and stayed there until the 31st apart from a short interlude with slightly cooler south-easterly winds on the 27th and 28th.

April. A warm and exceptionally dry month.

After an unsettled first day, pressure rose quite rapidly and by the 3rd an anticyclone lay over the British Isles. This brought sunny and relatively warm weather with cool nights for Holy Week culminating in an exceptionally mild and sunny Easter holiday weekend. Temperatures reached 16°C at Parkhead on Saturday 5th. The anticyclone drifted westwards into the Atlantic after the 7th bringing in air from a more northerly or north-westerly direction. Although daytime temperatures fell to 9.9°C by the 10th nights were milder. As the anticyclone moved back eastwards across southern Britain into Western Europe, a southerly airstream brought cloudy but extremely warm weather. Maximum temperatures on the 13th rose to 17.6°C at Parkhead and 17.7°C at the Ochil station. The temperature of 20°C recorded at Edinburgh Airport was the highest recorded in April since records began in 1949. The first rain in April, albeit only slight, occurred on the 14th as a weak warm front moved westwards across Scotland. As pressure fell over Europe an anticyclone developed to

10 the west of Britain and a cool northerly airstream became established. Weak frontal troughs moved south-eastwards on the 21st and 22nd as the weather pattern over the Atlantic was temporarily disrupted and brought a small amount of rain, but otherwise April continued to be dry.

May. Dry and sunny month.

The month began with high pressure to the north of Scotland and cool north-easterly winds from Scandinavia. Night-time temperatures eventually fell to -0.6°C and there followed 3 consecutive night frosts. Fortunately, this pattern began to break up on the 8th and high pressure became established over the North Sea on the 9th, moving to Scandinavia by the 11th. The imported warm Mediterranean air brought about a sharp increase in daytime temperatures under relatively clear skies. Maximum temperatures at Parkhead remained above 20°,C from the 11th to the 19th. Night-time temperatures however, fell but remained a degree or two above freezing. A south-eastwards moving trough of low pressure approached Scotland on the 19th, crossing the country on the 20th. This brought very slight rain (0.5 mm) to both Parkhead and the Ochil station, and was accompanied by a drop in daytime temperature. With the restoration of high pressure to the north-west of Britain on the 21st, skies cleared and temperatures again rose to over 20°C on the 23rd and 24th, although there was a fresh northerly wind. High pressure moved away westwards on the 25th and for the remainder of the month the weather was dominated by unsettled cyclonic conditions. A slow-moving cold front brought the month's wettest day on the 27th, precipitation occurring as snow in parts of the Highlands.

June. Cool, wet and unsettled.

The month saw the beginning and the end as far as summer was concerned. During the first four days, pressure remained high to the south and south-east of Britain bringing mild south-westerly winds across Scotland. Rain fell from an eastwards moving warm front which crossed the country on the 2nd and 3rd. High pressure over the North Sea on the 4th brought a warm southerly airstream across Scotland and daytime temperatures rose to the month's highest value at Parkhead of 24.8°C, and 25.5°C at the Ochil station. Temperatures in the upper 20's were recorded in many parts of Scotland. Daytime temperatures decreased after the 5th as unsettled weather patterns developed bringing occasional thundery outbreaks of rain to much of Britain. As a depression moved northwards from France into Scotland on the 14th torrential rain fell as far north as the Borders. Stirling escaped the worst of the rain but nevertheless

received about 16 mm in 24 hours. A succession of frontal troughs **11**
ensured rainfall on all but three of the remaining days of the month.
Westerly gales were experienced as a vigorous depression moved
across northern Scotland between the 18th and 20th but rainfall was
slight. Monthly rainfall was nearly 50 per cent higher than average at
Parkhead.

July. Cool and wet.
   A ridge of high pressure to the west of the country brought cool
northerly air to Scotland on the 1st but by the 3rd this had given
way to a more unsettled weather pattern which persisted until the
6th. A weak ridge of high pressure developed over the northern
Atlantic along longitude 30°W on the 7th resulting in a cool
relatively dry northerly airflow over Scotland. The ridge was breached
on the 11th bringing a milder westerly interlude for four days, after
which cooler air returned. Unsettled weather returned on the 17th
bringing cloud and rain as frontal troughs moved across Scotland.
Drier more settled weather on the 20th and 21st was associated with
an area of high pressure which moved eastwards off the south coast
of England. As this proceeded northwards into Germany and
Scandinavia, Britain experienced the warmest weather of the month
after the 23rd. Temperatures in England reached 29°C on the 25th.
Scotland, however, saw little of the sun as Atlantic fronts moved
across bringing cloud and rain. The heaviest rain of the month
occurred on the 30th as a cold front moved northwards across the
country. Temperatures reached the month's highest on the 28th at
Parkhead (23.1^{O}C) and Ochil (21°C) stations.

August. Damp but relatively mild.
   With high pressure over central and western Europe, mild
southerly air affected Scotland for the first three days. Heavy,
sometimes thundery rain fell on the 2nd bringing 10 mm to Parkhead
but only 6 mm to the Ochil station. As a ridge of high pressure
developed to the west, Scotland experienced its coldest day of the
month on the 7th although the north-easterly winds remained light.
High pressure lingered until the 10th when less settled weather
returned bringing rain and fresh south-westerly winds. Fronts crossing
Scotland on the 13th and 14th brought some of the wettest weather
of the month. Unsettled weather prevailed until the 21st when
pressure began to increase to the west. Winds veered to northerly and
became light and the next six days, for a change, remained quite dry.
However, night-time temperatures fell quite sharply, falling to 2.6^{O}C
at Parkhead, and 1.0^{O}C at Carim on the 22nd. Slight ground frosts
were noted in some localities. As the anticyclone moved into the
Continent and began to break up, frontal troughs accompanied by

12 fresh westerly winds brought rain on the 28th. Heavy rain fell on the 29th which was the wettest day of the month. 18 mm of rain was measured at Carim station. The month ended with the promise of more settled weather as a ridge of high pressure moved eastwards over Britain.

September. Mild and rainy.

Any hopes of a late summer were finally squashed as rain swept across Scotland on 22 of the 30 days of September. Temperatures remained relatively high for a while as high pressure persisted over northern France and southern England, but frontal troughs were accompanied by freshening winds and rain on the 4th. A vigorous depression and associated fronts gave Scotland strong westerly winds and rain on the 6th and 7th while most of southern England remained relatively dry until the 8th when a cold front affected these areas. On the 11th and 12th a deep depression which had merged with a decaying tropical storm moved across northern Scotland bringing strong winds and driving rain. 19.1 mm of rain fell at Parkhead on the 11th while at the Ochil station 27.5 mm was recorded. Yet more rain was to follow on the 13th as the next frontal systems in what seemed to be an endless queue dropped a further 11.6 mm of rain on the University. The weather remained unsettled and wet and on the 17th a deep Atlantic depression approached Britain which fortunately filled as it progressed eastwards. It nevertheless brought a further 9.5 mm of rain to the Ochil station. After a brief respite from the rain on the 19th and 20th, frontal systems brought slight rain after the 21st. The weather was particularly unsettled on the 26th as a warm front trailed eastwards across Scotland. Although only 5.9 mm of rain were recorded at Parkhead, 32.5 mm fell on the hill catchment, the highest daily total of the year. While southern England remained dry after the 24th, it was not until the 27th that somewhat drier weather came to Scotland. Despite a fresh westerly wind the clear skies of the 27th and 28th were a pleasant change. This brief interlude ended abruptly as further cloud and rain spread from the west on the 29th.

October. Cold, wet and windy.

Summer now seemed to be merging with the oncoming winter. To the wet weather, which had continued to be the main characteristic of the 1980 summer, were added the first air frosts of the winter. The first few days offered us stark contrasts in the weather. Strong westerly winds on the 1st gradually died away overnight and were replaced by calm clear anticyclonic weather on the 2nd. On the 3rd, warm and cold fronts crossed Scotland and heavy rain was recorded. Clear skies returned on the 4th but a fresh north-westerly wind kept

temperatures down. A vigorous depression crossed northern Scotland **13**
on the 5th and 6th. Strong westerly winds and intermittent rain
persisted for the two days. As its eastwards movement slowed down
as it approached Scandinavia, the depression remained the dominant
influence on Scottish weather until the 9th, but no further rain fell.
A deep depression which moved eastwards up the English Channel on
the 10th and 11th resulted in heavy rain and low temperatures in
southern and central England but for once the tables were turned.
Scotland remained cool and dry. As winds veered to the north on the
11th, night-time temperatures fell sharply and the first air frost of
the winter was recorded at Parkhead although this was only -0.5°C.
Temperatures as low as -5°C were recorded in parts of Scotland.
The south of England again experienced rain as another depression
travelled up the English Channel after the 15th, deepening as it
approached Denmark. Only a small amount of rain fell in central
Scotland. Between the 18th and 20th Britain lay in the col between
high pressure to north and south. Under relatively clear skies
night-time temperatures fell to 0°C on three nights, reaching -3.6°C
at Parkhead on the morning of the 20th (only 1.0°C at Carim). A
warm front advanced northwards on the 20th bringing rain later in
the day. The weather remained unsettled with occasionally heavy rain
until the 28th when pressure began to rise. Heavy rain occurred over
most of Scotland on the 22nd and 23rd some of which fell as snow
on high ground.

November. Cool then mild. Generally wet.

High pressure over the Baltic and low pressure over Portugal
dominated the weather over Britain for the first three days. Winds
over Scotland were southerly, decreasing to light and variable by the
3rd. As the anticyclone moved westwards out into the Atlantic it
passed to the north of Scotland bringing most of the country into a
cool easterly airstream. Night-time temperatures however, fell below
0°C on only one occasion, on the 3rd. A weak cold front moved
southwards on the 8th but brought no rain to the Stirling area.
Another which affected Scotland on the 10th brought a small
amount of rain. As High 'P' drifted south from the Iceland area into
the Bay of Biscay, Britain was brought under the influence of
westerly weather on the 13th. Winds became fresh westerly and
rainfall was at times heavy. 10.5 mm fell on the University on the
13th, 17.5 mm on the Ochil station. One of the wettest days of the
month was the 16th, when 11.9 mm and 23.5 mm respectively were
recorded at the two stations. This unsettled but mild weather
continued until the 25th by which time an extensive area of high
pressure had built up over the Atlantic. Fronts moved

14 south-eastwards across the country on the 25th and 26th bringing rain to most parts. Temperatures fell as a northerly airstream became established on the 26th, the air originating over the Arctic Ocean. On the 28th, a fresh northerly wind combined with a maximum daytime temperature of only 4.5°C at Parkhead (0.2°C at Ochil station) to produce extremely chilling conditions. High 'D' which became stationary over the British Isles on the 29th had a centre pressure of 1046 mb, the highest recorded since December, 1962.

December. Cold, damp and windy.

A frontal trough moving south-eastwards across Scotland on the 1st brought slight amounts of rain to the Stirling area. As High 'D' became stationary over the Atlantic to the west of the country northerly weather affected Scotland until the 6th. A southwards moving cold front crossed the Stirling area early on the 5th but no rainfall was recorded. On the 6th and 7th High 'I' moved south-eastwards across Britain and was centred over France by the 8th. Nocturnal temperatures fell below freezing on the 6th and 7th while daytime temperatures reached only 4.4°C at Parkhead on the 7th in a fresh northerly wind. At Carim air temperatures stayed at or below freezing point for 72 hours! As the high moved into the Mediterranean, unsettled Atlantic weather patterns returned to Scotland. The weather remained unsettled for most of the remainder of the month. The month's wettest day occurred on the 14th as a deep depression moved rapidly across Scotland. A small ridge of high pressure moved across between the 18th and 19th and overnight temperatures fell to −2.5°C at Parkhead (−5.0°C at Ochil station). An occluded front brought overnight snow to Scotland which was still lying at 9 a.m. on the 20th. It lay for two more days before disappearing from lowland areas. Snow showers occurred on both the 25th and 26th but a white Christmas was not to be, except on high ground. Westerly gales, occasionally reaching storm force affected Scotland over the last three days of 1980 and the New Year was seen in to blizzard conditions.

Climatological averages for Parkhead

Climatological averages are usually taken over periods of 30 years in the case of temperature and 35 years in the case of rainfall. This is because, in Britain, there is a built-in year to year variation in all the parameters which we use to define climate. If we use too small a number of years our average may be biased by one extreme value. As there are only 10 years of records for Parkhead there is, therefore, considerable room for error in the calculation of averages. The table of climatological averages for this station should, therefore, be viewed with some caution.

	Mean °C Maximum	Diff. from Average	Highest Maximum	Lowest Maximum	Mean °C Minimum	Diff. from Average	Highest Minimum	Lowest Minimum	Mean °C	Number of Air Frosts	Mean Earth Temp. °C
January	4.6	− 1.2	8.0	1.0	− 0.8	− 1.2	4.0	− 6.5	1.9	14	1.1
February	7.0	+ 0.7	11.0	0.8	2.0	+ 1.2	6.5	− 5.0	4.5	8	3.0
March	7.3	− 1.3	11.0	2.9	0.3	− 1.3	5.5	− 4.6	3.8	12	3.7
April	13.4	+ 1.8	17.6	8.7	3.5	+ 0.3	7.9	0.5	8.4	0	7.7
May	17.1	+ 2.0	24.8	10.1	3.7	− 1.6	9.2	− 0.6	10.4	3	11.8
June	16.3	− 1.2	24.8	11.0	8.3	+ 0.4	15.0	5.2	12.3	0	14.5
July	18.3	− 1.4	23.1	14.3	9.1	− 1.5	15.2	4.0	13.7	0	15.3
August	18.4	− 0.4	21.1	14.6	10.2	+ 0.3	15.8	2.6	14.3	0	16.0
September	16.5	+ 0.5	19.4	13.1	9.1	+ 0.7	13.8	4.3	12.8	0	14.2
October	11.2	− 1.6	16.0	5.4	4.0	− 2.0	9.4	− 3.6	7.6	5	9.1
November	9.2	+ 0.5	13.4	4.4	2.9	+ 0.6	9.6	− 4.0	6.0	7	6.3
December	8.0	+ 0.8	12.3	1.4	2.3	+ 0.4	8.5	− 2.7	5.2	11	3.9
Year	12.3	0	24.8	0.8	4.6	− 0.3	15.8	− 6.5	8.4	60	8.9

Monthly Temperatures (Stirling, Parkhead) 1980

S. J. Harrison

	Mean °C Maximum	Highest Maximum	Lowest Maximum	Mean °C Minimum	Highest Minimum	Lowest Minimum	Mean °C	Number of Air Frosts	Mean Relative Humidity 0900
January	—	—	—	—	—	—	—	—	
February	—	—	—	—	—	—	—	—	
March	—	—	—	—	—	—	—	—	
April	—	—	—	—	—	—	—	—	76
May	13.9	21.5	7.7	2.9	8.0	− 2.0	8.4	5	74
June	13.5	22.5	8.0	6.9	15.9	2.4	10.2	0	79
July	14.3	21.0	8.8	7.7	14.7	2.5	11.0	0	79
August	15.3	19.0	11.5	9.3	13.9	1.0	12.3	0	82
September	13.1	16.0	10.8	9.1	12.2	5.8	11.1	0	89
October	7.7	11.6	4.0	3.5	9.5	− 0.5	5.6	3	84
November	5.0	10.1	0.2	1.2	7.5	− 4.0	3.1	13	84
December	4.3	8.5	− 1.0	0.5	6.5	− 5.0	2.4	16	85

Monthly Temperatures (Ochil Hills, Carim) 1980

	Total Precipitation (mm)	Difference from Average (1971–80)	Greatest Fall in 24 hours		Precipitation Recorded	Number of days		
			Amount (mm)	Date		0.2mm or more	1.0mm or more	5.0mm or more
January	63.4	− 37.2	14.5	3rd	13	13	11	4
February	80.0	+ 9.2	14.0	9th	18	17	16	7
March	80.1	+ 9.0	11.2	17th	19	19	18	6
April	3.7	− 36.4	1.2	14th	4	4	2	0
May	9.7	− 45.6	6.3	27th	6	5	2	1
June	75.4	+ 23.9	15.9	14th	19	19	15	6
July	50.3	+ 11.5	13.2	30th	19	17	9	4
August	57.7	− 4.3	12.4	29th	15	15	12	4
September	88.3	+ 12.5	19.1	11th	22	22	17	9
October	79.0	+ 3.6	12.9	6th	19	16	14	7
November	125.5	+ 25.8	13.0	25th	19	18	16	9
December	116.5	+ 30.0	16.9	14th	20	18	15	11
Year	829.6	− 21.0	19.1	11th Sept.	193	183	147	68

Monthly Precipitation (Stirling, Parkhead) 1980

	Total Precipitation (mm)	Greatest Fall in 24 Hours Amount (mm)	Date	Number of Days 0.5mm or more	1.0mm or more	5.0mm or more
January	—	—	—	—	—	—
February	—	—	—	—	—	—
March	—	—	—	—	—	—
April	1.5	0.5	22nd 24th 29th	3	0	0
May	17.0	9.0	27th	8	3	1
June	74.0	11.5	5th	18	16	7
July	116.5	23.0	3rd	19	16	9
August	79.0	18.0	29th	17	16	6
September	183.5	32.5	26th	24	23	14
October	105.0	21.0	3rd	17	14	9
November	138.0	23.5	16th	20	17	12
December	193.0	22.0	14th	21	18	12

Monthly Precipitation (Ochil Hills, Carim) 1980

(*Instrument faulty)

	Maximum Air Temperature °C	Minimum Air Temperature °C	Number of Air Frosts	Earth Temperature 30cm (0900)	Total Precipitation (mm)	Number of days with precipitation
January	5.8	0.4	13	3.0	100.6	19
February	6.3	0.8	11	2.8	70.8	17
March	8.6	1.6	9	4.3	71.1	17
April	11.6	3.2	3	7.5	40.1	12
May	15.1	5.3	2	11.4	55.3	14
June	17.5	7.9	0	14.4	51.5	14
July	19.7	10.6	0	16.4	61.8	13
August	18.8	9.9	0	16.2	62.0	14
September	16.0	8.4	0	13.6	75.8	15
October	12.8	6.0	3	10.3	75.4	15
November	8.7	2.3	9	6.0	99.7	18
December	7.2	1.9	10	3.8	86.5	18
Year	12.3	4.9	60	9.1	850.6	186

Climatological Averages for Stirling (Parkhead)
University of Stirling 1971—1980

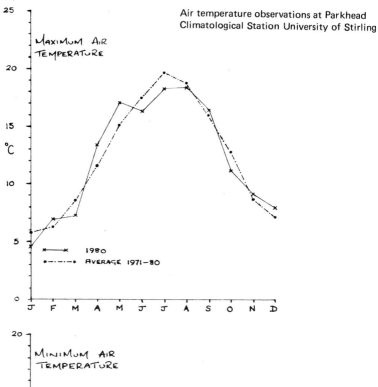

Air temperature observations at Parkhead
Climatological Station University of Stirling

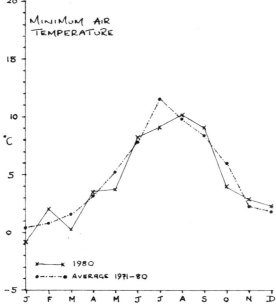

Observations at Parkhead Climatological
Station University of Stirling

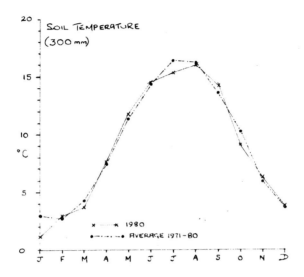

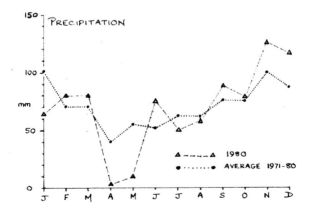

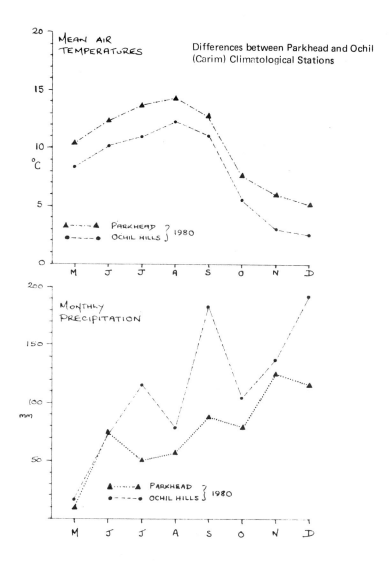

MEAN AIR TEMPERATURES

Differences between Parkhead and Ochil (Carim) Climatological Stations

MONTHLY PRECIPITATION

RAINFALL IN THE STIRLING AREA   **23**

S. J. Harrison
University of Stirling

THE NATURE OF RAINFALL

Rainfall is strictly defined as that part of precipitated atmospheric water which reaches the Earth's surface in a liquid form, in contrast to ice forms such as hail and snow. However, for practical purposes, the term rainfall normally embraces all water which is collected in a standard rain collector or rain gauge. Some of this may well have fallen as ice but has since either melted away naturally, or has been melted by the rainfall observer at the time of observation. Rainfall results from those atmospheric processes which encourage extensive condensation of water vapour, and the growth of the resulting water droplets or ice crystals so that they fall towards the Earth's surface. As a component of the Scottish climate most rainfall is derived from either eastwards moving Atlantic depressions passing across the country, or from rapid localised convectional uplift in the atmosphere. Both these are subject to considerable modification by hills and mountains as air flows over and around them.

RAINFALL FORECASTING

Neither the location nor the timing of the occurrence of rainfall are particularly easy to predict. Forecasting rainfall has always been a difficult practice at anything other than short time scales. This is largely due to the complexity of the atmospheric processes at work, but more specifically to the not fully understood range of local factors such as topography.

At a local level, reliance has often been placed on an ability to interpret certain natural signals and upon established weather lore. Apart from the human body's own sensitivity to changes in atmospheric conditions in advance of rainfall, it is possible to detect behavioural changes in, for example, birds, animals and plants. This is well exemplified in the following nineteenth century poem by a Dr. Jenner, referred to by the Reverend Brotherston in the New Statistical Account of Scotland in 1845

The walls are damp, the ditches smell
Closed is the pink-eyed pimpernel
Loud quack the ducks, the sea-fowl cry
The distant hills are looking nigh

24 Low o'er the grass the swallow wings
The cricket too how loud it sings
The wind unsteady veers around
Or settling in the south is found
The whirling wind the dust obeys
And o'er the rapid eddy plays
The leech disturbed is newly risen
Quite to the summit of his prison

Reverend Brotherston also suggested a cheap device for predicting rainfall. This comprises a

'leech in an eight ounce phial glass, three fourths filled with water, covered with a piece of linen rag and kept in a cool place, the water being changed once a week in summer and once a fortnight in winter. In serene weather and during frost, the leech lies at the bottom of the glass, rolled together in a spiral form. Before rain or snow it creeps to the top of its lodging and there remains till the weather is settled. Before wind it appears in rapid motion. Some time before thunder and rain it remains almost constantly above the water and appears in great uneasiness'.

For most areas there is a traditional weather lore, often relating to particular landscape features. Harvey (1900) gives us two examples for the Stirling area

When the castle of Stirling gets a hat (low cloud)
The carse of Cornton pays for that (rain falls)

and

When the mist taks the hills (Ochils)
Guid weather spills (rain is due)
When the mist taks the howes (Hillfoots)
Guid weather grows (stable, fine weather is due)

While most of these are based upon several generations of experience of weather changes in the local area and are meteorologically sound, some, however, seem to have no meteorological basis whatsoever. For example, Harvey also writes that

'. . . the third Tuesday in June is inseparably associated with rain. Bannockburn Fair falls on that day and rain is always expected'.

THE RAINFALL RECORD

In order to examine the characteristics of rainfall over an area, it is essential to devise methods of measuring how much falls on the ground surface. The earliest British observations were made in the late seventeenth century by a Mr Townley of Burnley, Lancashire. During the eighteenth century increasing numbers of raingauges were installed in, for example, parks and ornamental gardens, hospital

grounds, churchyards, and private gardens, but in the absence of any **25**
central co-ordination of data collection, many of these early
observations have been lost or remain undiscovered in private records.
There was also no standardisation of rainfall observation practice.
Many gauges were placed too near trees and houses which would
undoubtedly affect measured rainfall. Time of observation also varied
from gauge to gauge.

Weather observation in the nineteenth century came to be linked
very closely with medical science, particularly in the field of
epidemiology. For example, the high incidence during summer of a
fatal form of diarrhoea was found to be closely related to soil
temperatures which led to the establishment of many hospital
weather stations. The incidence of cholera outbreaks were closely
linked to the amount and distribution of water supply, and hence to
rainfall inputs. One of the first to realise this was G. J. Symons who,
in 1860, founded the British Rainfall Organisation and its
publication, *British Rainfall*. He enforced a rigorous standardisation
of raingauge sites and found a large number lacking. One gauge was
found to have over it a small roof to protect it from the rain. Others
were placed where intercepted water from trees could drip into them
resulting, in some instances, in fatal miscalculation of water supply.
Patrick Graham, in writing his *General View of the Agriculture of
Stirlingshire* in 1812, commented

'It is regretted that no register of the quantity of rain that falls in
this district annually has been discovered by the reporter.'

General observations of weather were, however, made in the late
eighteenth and early nineteenth century by Dr Macfarlane, the
minister of Drymen, who noted days upon which rain fell. The first
issue of *British Rainfall*, in 1860, contained observations from 168
raingauges of which none was from Scotland, but of the 471 entries
in 1861 some 109 were Scottish. By 1901 there were 3506 entries,
of which 442 were from Scotland, and by 1921 these figures had
increased to 784 out of 5079. (Meteorological Office 1922) Local
observers in the Forth Valley made a significant contribution during
this period of development.

THE STIRLING ORGANISATION

A local rainfall organisation was established in the late nineteenth
century by Colonel Stirling of Gargunnock House, which published
an annual digest in the *Transactions of the Stirling Natural History
and Archaeological Society*. From an early group of 14 in 1894, the
list grew to 24 by 1921, although not all were in the Forth Valley.

26 These are indicated on the map (Figure 1). The 1894 observers were drawn from all walks of life as is clearly shown in Table 1. The main features of rainfall variation in the Stirling area have been distilled from the long and uninterrupted record of monthly totals for Gargunnock House and Earlsburn, both of which submitted data to British Rainfall. There is, therefore, an assurance of a reasonable degree of accuracy in the observations.

Buchlyvie (The Manse)	Reverend John Alexander MacDonald	1894-1917
Earlsburn Reservoir	C. Massie Esq.	1894-1932
Gargunnock House	Established in the late nineteenth century by Colonel John Stirling, who retired from the Royal Artillery in 1879. He was an enthusiastic naturalist, making a major contribution, with Robert Kidston, to the study of local flora. Observations were continued by Charles Stirling after his death in May 1900.	1894-1938
Arngomery (Kippen)	Peter McCowan, head gardener.	1896-1929
Ochtertyre (Doune)	Commander Colin Mackenzie Dundas RN	1894-1911
Stirling (Victoria Place)	Dr Robert Kidston FRS, a well-known local figure noted for his work on fossil plants and local flora.	1894-1923
Touch Reservoir	A. H. Goudie	1914-1937
Touch House	Sir D. A. Seton-Stewart	1914-1921

Table 1   Noteworthy local rainfall observers in the late 19th and early 20th Century (from Transactions of the Stirling Natural History and Archaeological Society).

SEASONAL VARIATION IN RAINFALL

A rainfall dispersion diagram for Gargunnock (Figure 2) reveals variation from year to year in the amount of rain each month. Variability in monthly rainfall is indicated by the shaded area which contains all but the extreme highest and lowest fifths, or quintiles, of the range of values. From this it is apparent that rainfall in spring and early summer is less variable and, to some extent therefore, more predictable than during the winter months. The seasonal distribution **27** of mean monthly rainfall over the period 1894-1938 indicates a marked winter maximum in December and January, and a minimum in late spring and early summer. There is, however, a marked deviation from this simple pattern in August when average rainfall is considerably higher than in either July or September. Subjecting the data for Earlsburn Reservoir to a similar analysis also reveals this pattern of a drier season with lowest variability and a wetter season with more variation in rainfall (Figure 3). By ranking months in each year according to whether they had the highest (1) to lowest (12) total rainfall, and by determining the number of occasions when each month ranked amongst the two wettest or two driest over the period 1894 to 1938, this seasonality becomes clearer (Figure 4). At both Gargunnock and Earlsburn the wettest months occur most frequently during the winter, while the drier 'season' embraces February, March, April, May and June. Despite its relatively high average rainfall, August is rarely the wettest month of the year.

In the British Isles it is usual to have slightly more rainfall in winter when Atlantic depressions and their associated fronts frequently pass across the country. With the northwards shift in the track of depression movement during the summer, rainbearing weather is slightly less frequent. Lower rainfall in spring and early summer is a result of more stable atmospheric conditions associated with high pressure in the immediate vicinity of the British Isles.

While much of the high August rainfall is cyclonic in origin, there is a tendency towards a higher frequency of heavy rainstorms at this time of year, associated with locally vigorous uplift in the lower atmosphere. An analysis of daily rainfall totals for Touch Reservoir (Smith 1974) has indicated a tendency towards high values during August.

Around the turn of the century reports of exceptional weather frequently appeared in the Stirling Journal and Advertiser. Over the period 1870 to 1919 reports of exceptional thunderstorms or rainstorms appear in much greater frequency during the summer months, indicating locally strong convectional activity in the atmosphere at this time of year (Table 2).

Jan	Feb	Mar	Apr	May	Jun	Jul	Aug	Sept	Oct	Nov	Dec
9	4	4	2	6	19	20	17	8	5	6	5

Table 2   Published reference to thunderstorms and rainstorms in the Stirling area (Stirling Journal and Advertiser 1870-1919).

28   The use of newspaper reports for climatological work should, of course, be tempered with caution, in that heavy rainfalls may not be regarded as exceptional, or newsworthy, during the normally wet winter months. In the slightly drier summer months, heavy falls not only represent a greater deviation from a 'norm', but also have a greater perceived impact on human activity, particularly during holiday periods. Typical of these heavy summer storms was that referred to by David Morris (1899). An extremely heavy thunderstorm occurred at Shielbrae some 7.2km to the west of Stirling during August 1897. Morris described a particularly remarkable, if perhaps a little exaggerated, feature of this storm

'Shortly after the storm one of the shepherds walking on the hill about five in the afternoon saw what he supposed was a sheep lying on its back ... He thought the sheep might have been killed by lightning, but on approaching he discovered that it was a block of ice. It was as large as the body of a sheep and he estimated it to weigh about a hundredweight.'

This was probably an agglomeration of moderate sized hailstones resulting from strong turbulence and deep vertical currents in the atmosphere on that day.

RAINFALL DISTRIBUTION OVER THE STIRLING AREA

The map of rainfall distribution in the Stirling area (Figure 5) is based on a limited number and patchy distribution of raingauges. Constructing isohyets is more freqently inspired guesswork than an objective interpolation between data points. Nevertheless, the map does illustrate the two most important aspects of rainfall distribution which are a distinct west to east decrease, and a marked effect of elevation over the Ochil Hills, and the Touch and Gargunnock Hills. Rainbearing weather systems tend to deposit their moisture as they move in from the west, giving rise to the familiar contrast between wet west and dry east in the British Isles. However, the Central Lowlands of Scotland provide a natural corridor for westerly airstreams which means that Fife, for example, is wetter than would be regarded as typical of its easterly location. Knowledge of rainfall variation in hill areas is still relatively incomplete due, in large part, to a basic lack of rainfall observations. There is, for example, very little rainfall information for the Ochil Hills. The Stirling area is, however, fortunate in having long records from the North Third (175m above sea-level), Touch (139m) and Earlsburn (366m) Reservoirs in the Touch Hills. By comparing rainfall observations from Earlsburn and Colonel Stirling's Gargunnock House (26m) gauges over the period 1894 to 1938, it is possible to examine the

effect of the difference in elevation between them. **29**
While many comparisons between lowland and upland rainfall refer to gauges some considerable distance apart, only 5km separates Earlsburn and Gargunnock House. The problems of including a distance factor into the analysis are, therefore, avoided but it must be noted that at Gargunnock there is the possibility of a rain-shadow effect from the nearby hills.

A direct comparison of monthly averages at the two sites (Figure 6) confirms that rainfall is greater at Earlsburn than at Gargunnock, although seasonal variation is remarkably similar. In terms of average annual rainfall this represents a difference of 413.5mm (16.28 inches) between them or a rate of altitudinal increase of 133.5mm per 100m (14.67 inches per 1,000 feet). Applying this to Ben Cleuch (721m) in the Ochil Hills, this would imply an annual rainfall in excess of 1,900mm (75 inches) in contrast to the 1,000mm (40 inches) in Stirling.

A VALEDICTION

In analysing rainfall records of this antiquity it is usually wise to err on the side of caution. In some cases, largely unknown variation in observation practices can lead to the drawing of conclusions based upon apparent and not real differences in rainfall between sites. However, in the Stirling area there is a body of relatively reliable rainfall data collected by dedicated observers and collated by Colonel Stirling and his family. In the annual digest of rainfall statistics published in the *Transactions of the Stirling Natural History and Archaeological Society,* a form of quality control was exercised by the Stirlings.

There are still local observers, sadly now few in number, whose rainfall records are processed by the Meteorological Office in Edinburgh who carry out raingauge inspections, albeit infrequently. Sadly, *British Rainfall* has now died and has been replaced by the functional *Monthly and Annual Totals of Rainfall for the UK* published by the Meteorological Office. As to the local 'Stirling' rainfall organisation, this has long since disappeared and with it perhaps went a strong local tradition of dedicated rainfall observation.

REFERENCES

BROTHERSTON, P. 1845. The Parish of Alloa, The New Statistical Account of Scotland, volume VIII, Dumbarton, Stirling and Clackmannan. Blackwood, Edinburgh.

30 GRAHAM, P. 1812. General View of the Agriculture of Stirlingshire. Creech and Constable, Edinburgh.

HARVEY, W. 1900. Rhymes, proverbs and proverbial expressions of Stirling and district. *Transactions of the Stirling Natural History and Archaeological Society* 22, 10-11.

METEOROLOGICAL OFFICE. 1922. British Rainfall 1921, volume 61. British Rainfall Organisation, H.M.S.O., London.

MORRIS, D. 1899. Large hailstone at Sheilbrae. *Transactions of the Stirling Natural History and Archaeological Society* 21, 175.

SMITH, K. 1974. Climatology and hydrology, 49-65. The Stirling Region, editor D. W. G. Timms, Stirling University.

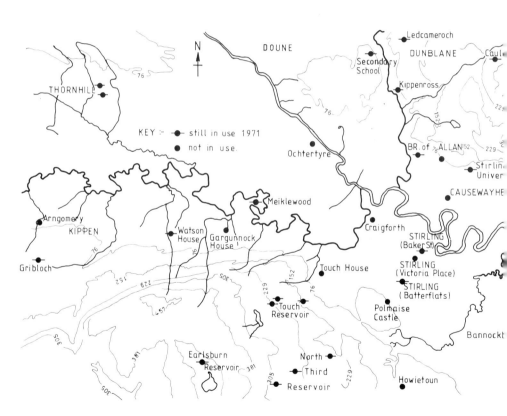

Figure 1   Raingauges in the Stirling Area

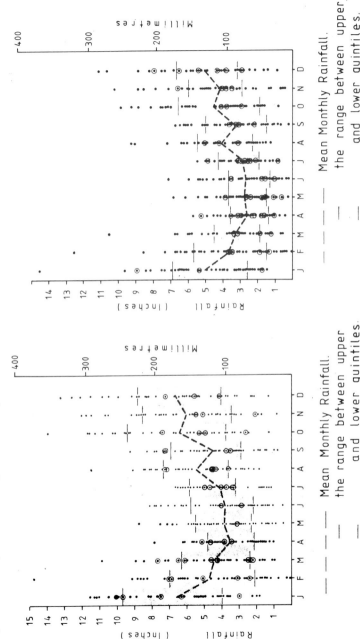

Figure 3 Monthly rainfall at Earslburn Reservoir, 1894-1938

Figure 2 Monthly rainfall at Gargunnock House, 1894-1938

Mean Monthly Rainfall.

the range between upper
and lower quintiles.

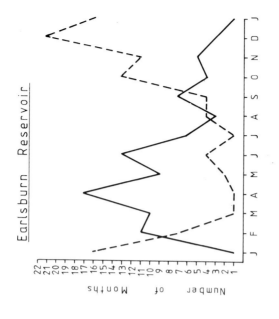

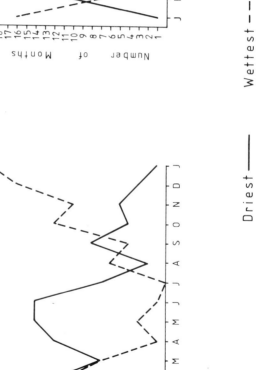

Figure 4 Number of occasions when months ranked amongst the two driest or wettest of individual years, 1894-1938

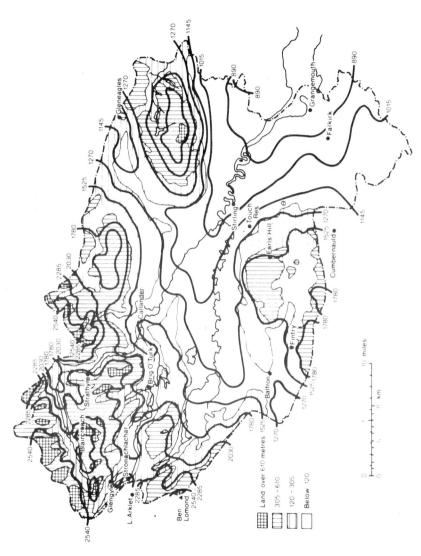

Figure 5   The distribution of mean annual precipitation in the Stirling
Region, 1916-1950 (after Smith, 1974)

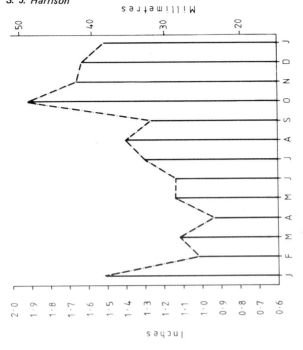

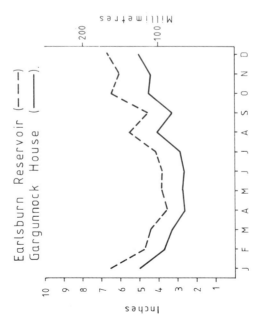

Earlsburn Reservoir (— — —).
Gargunnock House (————).

Figure 6 The effect of elevation upon rainfall. A comparison between Gargunnock House (26 m) and Earlsburn Reservoir (336 m)

FISH ENTRAINED IN 1977 AT COCKENZIE POWER STATION, 35
IN THE FIRTH OF FORTH

Peter S. Maitland, Kenneth East and Kenneth H. Morris
Institute of Terrestrial Ecology

INTRODUCTION

The phenomenon of the entrainment of fish at the intake works to power stations is becoming a well known one, and the factors related to entrainment and to the subsequent fate of entrained fish are now the subject of a considerable amount of research in many parts of the world (Thorpe and Gibbons 1978). The requirement of almost all kinds of electricity generating power stations (coal, oil and nuclear) for very large amounts of water for cooling purposes has meant that all of them are situated beside large bodies of water — the sea, estuaries, large rivers or large lakes. Though it is possible to screen the intake tunnels to such power stations in various ways it is virtually inevitable that zooplankton, other larger invertebrates and small fish are entrained and passed into the stations.

Most stations have a further form of screening through which the water passes, usually after it has been chlorinated, and this removes the bulk of larger particles and animals in the water, which then passes through the cooling system of the station itself. Screened fish and other objects are washed into trash baskets which require to be emptied regularly. There is often a very high mortality among animals which are entrained due to the chlorination, the mechanical effects of screening or passage through the water ducting system, and the thermal effect of raised temperatures after passing through the condensers. In the case of pumped-storage hydro-electric power stations no chlorination nor temperature effects are involved and damage to fish is usually mechanical or hydrostatic.

Originally most of the research on fish at such power stations was of a purely applied nature and related to operational problems (e.g. the actual blockage of intakes or cooling systems by fish, thereby causing shutdowns and financial loss), or to ecological problems, the main concern here being the impact of mortalities caused by the power station on the local fish populations. However, in recent years power station intakes have been recognised as having considerable value to biologists and much of the present research is directed at examining the value of screen catches as a biological method of monitoring water quality or of studying the population dynamics of various species (e.g. Claridge and Gardner 1978).

36   During initial studies of the distribution of fish in the British Isles
(Maitland 1969) it was quickly apparent that very little information
existed on the fish communities of certain habitats, particularly large
rivers and estuaries. In Scotland, relatively little was known about
any of the four major estuaries there — Forth, Tay, Moray or Clyde.
In the Firth of Forth for example, several fish known to be common
more than 100 years ago (Maitland 1979) now appear (from the few
data available) to be scarce or absent. Thus the Smelt *Osmerus*
eperlanus (Linnaeus 1758), was formerly very abundant in the Forth
(Parnell 1838), but there appeared to be no recent records. It was
believed that the examination of fish catches at power stations in the
area would be an economical and efficient way of assessing the status
of fish populations in the areas as has been clearly shown for the
River Thames by Wheeler (1969a).

SITE AND METHODS

In the first year of study (1977) it was decided to carry out a
pilot project at just one of the Forth power stations, and Cockenzie
was chosen as being the most suitable. Like the power station at
Leven on the opposite (north) side of the estuary, Cockenzie power
station is situated on the open seaward end of the estuary, where
tidal and salinity conditions are more or less fully marine (McLusky
1978). This is in contrast to the two power stations further west
(Kincardine and Longannet) which are more influenced by fresh
water.

Cockenzie is a 1200 megawatt, coal-fired power station, built on
the southern shore of the Firth of Forth about 16km east of
Edinburgh. It occupies a site covering in all some 93 hectares (ha).
The main buildings are to the north of the coast road on an area of
24 ha, half of which was reclaimed from the sea. South of the road
are the coal store, railway sidings, and the 275 kV switch-house.
Work on site began in January, 1962 and Cockenzie Power Station
was formally opened in May, 1968.

The cooling-water intake is set some 150m outside the sea wall in
a minimum depth of 4.6m at low tide. Water is drawn into vertical
shafts, of 4.3m diameter, which are joined to twin tunnels driven
24.4m below sea level. Coarse screens at the intake head-works
inhibit the passage of extraneous matter, and chlorine points prevent
mussel-fouling. Fine screening is carried out at the pumphouse. Some
$136000m^3$ (30 million gallons) an hour of chlorinated seawater are
passed through the steam-condensers for cooling purposes. In addition
there is a daily requirement of $2955m^3$ (650000 gallons) of domestic

water to provide make-up feedwater for the boilers. While Cockenzie Power Station is built on a site covering 93 ha, ash from the spent fuel is being used elsewhere to reclaim more than 110 ha from the sea. When it is considered that 12 ha of the station's main building area also were recovered from below tide-level it is plain that the net loss of ground to the firth is 122 ha.

Collections of fish were made at Cockenzie on ten different dates during 1977, normally in the morning between 0900-1000h. When possible, six different samples were taken — one from the channels and trash basket associated with each of the six screens. On several occasions, however, individual screens were not operating and fewer than six samples were obtained. Fish were collected by examining material from the channels and baskets in a systematic way until a total of 100 fish had been collected. The time taken to collect this number, or the whole sample if fewer than 100 fish were available, was recorded. The trash collected by the screens include a wide variety of other organisms (mussels, shrimps, crabs, seaweed etc.) as well as miscellaneous rubbish (plastic bottles, paper etc.).

The samples were taken back to the laboratory where the fish were washed, sorted and identified. The fork lengths of a random sample of 20 of each species in each sample were measured. Type specimens of all species were preserved for subsequent checking and the remainder of the collection discarded. No systematic records of weight or sex were kept, but regular notes were taken of unusual species, obvious parasites etc. The nomenclature used here is after Wheeler (1969b).

RESULTS

The main results from the 1977 collections are given in Tables 1 and 2. It can be seen that a total of 28 different species was recorded, but that the total catch was dominated by relatively few species — notably Sprat, Herring, Whiting and Sand Goby. Some species were recorded only occasionally, e.g. Eel, Weever, Painted Goby etc.

No attempt was made to quantify the catch involved at this power station and so there is no information on the total numbers entrained. The numbers included in Table 2 are intended solely to indicate the relative abundance of each species compared to the others and the relative number of occasions each species occurred in the total number of samples collected. In general it is true to say that the most abundant species also occurred on the highest number of occasions, and vice versa.

38   Seasonal information on the numbers of fish collected and the number of species identified on each sampling date is shown in Figure 2. It is clear that far more individuals and species were entrained during the colder winter months of the year than during the warmer summer months. Numbers were particularly high at the beginning of 1977.

The sizes of some of the fish collected are given in Figure 3. For the most part, the fish involved are rather small, representing the full range of size of the smaller species (e.g. Sand Goby) but probably only the smaller (and presumably younger — perhaps first and second year classes) of the larger species (e.g. Whiting). The length distribution of the four most abundant species in January 1977 is shown in Figure 3.

CLUPEIDAE
    Sprattus sprattus   Sprat
    Clupea harengus   Herring

ANGUILLIDAE
    Anguilla anguilla   Eel

SYNGNATHIDAE
    Syngnathus acus   Great Pipefish
    Entelurus aequoreus   Snake Pipefish

GADIDAE
    Merlangius merlangus   Whiting
    Pollachius virens   Saithe
    Gadus morhua   Cod
    Raniceps raninus   Tadpole-fish
    Ciliata mustela   Five-bearded Rockling

AMMODYTIDAE
    Ammodytes tobianus   Sand Eel
    Hyperoplus lanceolatus   Greater Sand Eel

TRACHINIDAE
    Trachinus vipera   Weever

GOBIIDAE
Pomatoschistus pictus   Painted Goby
Pomatoschistus minutus   Sand Goby

PHOLIDIDAE
Pholis gunnellus   Butterfish

ZOARCIDAE
Zoarces viviparus   Eelpout

MUGILIDAE
Crenimugil labrosus   Thick-lipped Mullet

COTTIDAE
Myoxocephalus scorpius   Bull Rout
Taurulus bubalis   Sea Scorpion

AGONIDAE
Agonus cataphractus   Pogge

CYCLOPTERIDAE
Cyclopterus lumpus   Lumpsucker

LIPARIDAE
Liparis liparis   Sea Snail
Liparis montagui   Montagu's Sea Snail

GASTEROSTEIDAE
Spinachia spinachia   Fifteen-spined Stickleback

PLEURONECTIDAE
Limanda limanda   Dab
Platichthys flesus   Flounder
Pleuronectes platessa   Plaice

TABLE 1   Check list of fish caught on Cockenzie Power Station Screens in 1977 (Nomenclature after Maitland (1972))

Species	% of Catch	% of Occurrences
Sprat	18.1	71.1
Herring	18.1	71.1
Eel	0.2	11.1
Great Pipefish	0.6	17.8
Snake Pipefish	0.1	4.4
Whiting	8.4	60.0
Saithe	0.7	22.2
Cod	0.3	15.5
Tadpole-fish	0.03	2.2
Five-bearded Rockling	1.1	26.7
Sand Eel	4.2	62.2
Greater Sand Eel	0.3	13.3
Weever	0.03	2.2
Painted Goby	0.03	2.2
Sand Goby	35.0	84.4
Butterfish	0.5	15.5
Eelpout	5.9	51.1
Thick-lipped Mullet	0.03	2.2
Bull Rout	0.1	6.6
Sea Scorpion	0.3	15.5
Pogge	2.8	48.9
Lumpsucker	0.03	2.2
Sea Snail	0.1	6.7
Montagu's Sea Snail	0.1	4.4
Fifteen-spined Stickleback	0.2	11.1
Dab	1.4	26.7
Flounder	0.9	24.4
Plaice	0.6	20.0
Totals	2956	46

TABLE 2   Composition of fish catch at Cockenzie in 1977 expressed as a % of the total number collected and a % of the total number of occurrences in screen collections.

DISCUSSION

One of the problems of interpreting fish catch data from power stations is to know just what they mean in terms of the natural fish population of the estuary itself. Short-term and long-term changes in the amounts of water pumped through the screens, in winds, tides and temperatures, and in both inter- and intra-specific behaviour (which may change seasonally) of the fish themselves, can lead to difficulties of interpretation. The quantification of data in particular, is often very difficult. In this premlininary study therefore, interpretation is restricted to simple aspects of the data, which are hopefully more or less free of the problems noted above.

The total number of species recorded in 1977 from the Firth of Forth at Cockenzie was 28. This is very many fewer than the 125 recorded in total for the estuary as a whole (Parnell 1838) but compares favourably with the 24 species recorded recently from regular Agassiz trawling at various places between Longannet and Aberlady (Dr M. Poxton personal communication). This confirms recent work reported by the Central Electricity Generating Board that power station intakes are relatively unselective. They are certainly far less demanding in terms of fisheries man-power.

With the exception of Eel, Thick-lipped Mullet and Flounder all the fish collected were purely marine species. All Eels and many Flounders though hatched in the sea do spend some time in freshwater — up to 25 years in the case of the former species, but naturally pass through estuaries travelling to and from the sea. Many Flounders and most Mullets spend the greater part of their lives in or near estuaries and are typical members of the fauna there. It is of interest to note that although only one Mullet was collected. at Cockenzie during 1977, these fish are commonly caught by anglers fishing near the heated effluent discharged from the power station.

Few of the marine species call for special comment. Sprat are known to be abundant in the Firth of Forth and form the basis of a fishery there. Herring on the other hand, though once caught in large numbers in the area (Thomas and Saville 1972) are now relatively unimportant. All the species concerned are indicated by Wheeler (1978) as occurring in inshore areas along this part of the British coast, with the exception of the Snake Pipefish, which is mainly an off-shore oceanic species and the Painted Goby which is supposed not to enter estuaries. However, both species were really rather rare at Cockenzie.

The work reported here was continued and extended in 1979 to cover three power stations in the Firth of Forth — at Cockenzie, Longannet and Kincardine. The data from these more recent comparative collections are at present being analysed and will be reported in a future paper. In addition, in that paper it is hoped to describe some much earlier unpublished work carried out in the early 1960's at Kincardine power station by the Department of Agriculture and Fisheries for Scotland.

42   In general, the composition of the fish catch at the three power stations (Cockenzie, Longannet and Kincardine) is similar — but there are certain consistent differences. For instance species with strong freshwater affinities are very rarely found at Cockenzie, but are taken regularly at Longannet and Kincardine. Lampreys, Trout and Eels, which all spend part of their lives in fresh waters and part in salt water, come into this category.

ACKNOWLEDGEMENTS

We are grateful to the South of Scotland Electricity Board for permission to visit the power station at Cockenzie during 1977. In particular, we would like to thank Mr M. Ilett and Mr Burdett for their help in arranging facilities there. Mr A. A. Lyle gave valuable help with the collecting of fish.

REFERENCES

CLARIDGE, P.N. and GARDNER, D.C. 1978. Growth and movements of the Twaite shad *Alosa fallax* (Lacepede) in the Severn Estuary. *Journal of Fish Biology* 12, 203-211.

McLUSKY, D.S. 1978. Ecology of the Forth estuary. *Forth Naturalist and Historian* 3, 10-23.

MAITLAND, P.S. 1969. A preliminary account of the mapping of the distribution of freshwater fish in the British Isles. *Journal of Fish Biology* 1, 45-58.

MAITLAND, P.S. 1972. A key to the freshwater fishes of the British Isles, with notes on their distribution and ecology. *Scientific Publications of the Freshwater Biological Association* 27, 1-139.

MAITLAND, P.S. 1979. The freshwater fish fauna of the Forth area. *Forth Naturalist and Historian* 4, 33-47.

PARNELL, R. 1838. Fishes of the district of the Firth of Forth. *Wernerian Natural History Society* 7, 161-520.

THOMAS, H.J. and SAVILLE, A. 1972. The fisheries of the Forth-Tay estuaries. *Proceedings of the Royal Society of Edinburgh* Section B 71, 171-188.

THORPE, J.H. and GIBBONS, J.W. 1978. Energy and Environmental Stress in Aquatic Systems. U.S. Department of Energy, Springfield, Virginia.

WHEELER, A.C. 1969a. Fish life and pollution in the lower Thames: a review and preliminary report. *Biological Conservation* 2, 25-30.

WHEELER, A.C. 1969b. The Fishes of the British Isles and North-west Europe. Macmillan, London.

WHEELER, A.C. 1978. Key to the Fishes of Northern Europe. Warne, London.

Figure 1 Map of part of the Firth of Forth showing the position of Cockenzie power station.

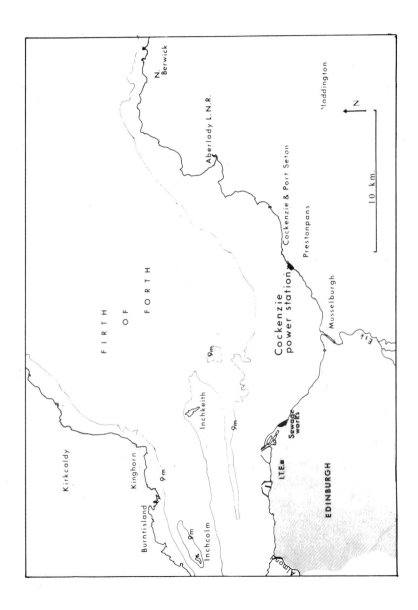

Figure 2 Numbers of fish per screen and numbers of species in each collection during 1977.

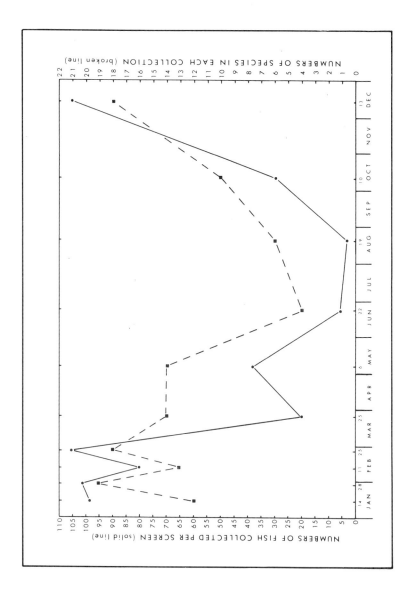

Figure 3 Length/frequency distributions of the four most abundant species in the collection taken on 28th January 1977.

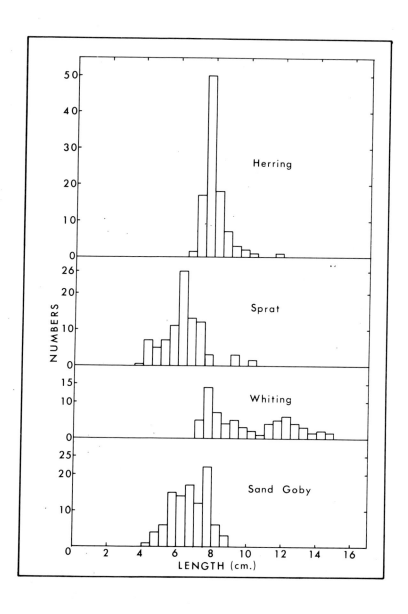

46   FORTH AREA BIRD REPORT
(CLACKS, STIRLING, SOUTHWEST PERTH) 1980

C. J. Henty
University of Stirling

Readers will notice that the title of this annual bird report has changed and that the notes on each species now include a section on southwest Perth. This decision to widen the area covered was the result of consultations between the editorial board of the Forth Naturalist, an informal group of local natural history recorders and the committee of the Stirling branch of the Scottish Ornithologists Club. It was agreed that the previous area was unsatisfactory for several reasons: it was a highly unnatural unit both from the ecological point of view and the activities of local observers, it was inconsistent with the boundary of the main historical source (Vertebrate Fauna of Forth) and furthermore quite different from the new administrative boundaries based on Districts — this was a real problem when conservation and planning issues came up. Thus I should like to receive in the future records from Clackmannanshire, east and central Stirlingshire (as far west as Carron Valley, Buchlyvie and Loch Ard Forest), and the new areas of southwest Perth — the Vale of Menteith, Trossachs, Balquhidder, Strathyre, Braes of Doune and Sheriffmuir. There is of course some overlap with the Perthshire bird report and I must emphasise that at present the areas of responsibility of the SOC official recorders remain unchanged, thus I guarantee to send on to the Perthshire recorder all relevant notes.

The final decision to include notes from southwest Perth was made and announced only in December, thus this 1980 report is not comprehensive. I hope the enlarged report will be more relevant to the interests of local observers and welcome notes for 1981 from old and new contributors. In the present report many notes are quoted as they were received but others are summarised or I have made the locality more general, either for brevity or because the original placename would be unknown to most readers. This could occasionally lead to the significance of a record being misinterpreted and I should like to be told of any serious problems.

The main features of the weather in 1980 were a long dry and warm spell through May followed by a notably unsettled and wet summer. Club members contributed to a weekend exploring Loch Ard Forest and also to the national survey of breeding waterfowl. It is worth drawing attention to the increasing evidence for a sizeable resident population of Crossbills in the west of the area. Our knowledge of the details of breeding distribution of several scarce **47** species remains meagre and, in particular, very few notes are received on the game birds. Ruffs came through in considerable numbers in September and the records of this and several other species suggest an inland passage of waders that is more important than might have been thought from previous records. The loss of marshy habitats in the Forth valley continues — the swampy meadows upstream of Cambus have been largely drained whilst the estuarine embayment at Blackdevonmouth has been converted to a dumping area for general refuse and also low grade radioactive waste.

The Scottish Wildlife Trust is organising the collection of records of Green Woodpecker, Magpie, Jay and Redstart to map their distributions more precisely. The assistance of all observers would be very much appreciated; please note occurrences of these species and pass on the information to W. R. Brackenridge or myself. Other species that I should especially like to have details about are:— Buzzard, Ptarmigan, Black Grouse, Capercaillie, Barn Owl, Great Spotted Woodpecker, Stonechat and Twite. Other topics worth recording include roosting, the occurrence in typical suburban/farmland species in remote areas and up highland glens, habitat distribution and the seasonal appearance and disappearance of species. It would help the recorder greatly if observers with many records could send most of them in before Christmas. This report has to be compiled in two or three weeks between mid January and mid February so that notes received after the middle of January cannot be given as much consideration as they may deserve and, if a typescript has already been completed, it may be impossible to insert them into the report although they will enter the main file of information.

As in previous years the notes on a particular species often have to be interpreted against a general background that is not summarised here — would it be worth producing a brief comprehensive summary of present distribution to supplement the information in the *BTO Atlas of Breeding Distribution* and D. M. Bryant's essay on local birds in *The Stirling Region*? An asterisk indicates where all records for a species have been quoted whilst the sections headed by C, S and SWP refer to notes for Clackmannan, Stirlingshire and southwest Perth respectively.

Species that have occurred in the area in 1980 but for which no notes are published : Red Grouse, Ptarmigan, Black Grouse, Pheasant, Capercaillie, Turnstone, Whinchat, Ring Ouzel, Spotted Flycatcher, Treecreeper, Jackdaw.

48 *RED-THROATED DIVER
S   1 dead at Skinflats on 16th March (DMB)

LITTLE GREBE
C   3 pairs at Gartmorn Dam in May, (broods seen (IN, WRB)
S   Airthrey Loch, 1st on 13th February, 2 pairs reared 1 Y (MWF,CJH)
SWP Pairs on L. Venachar, L. Dhu, Strathyre, new dam at Invertrossachs
       – young reared (WRB,DT)

GREAT CRESTED GREBE
C   2 pairs on Gartmorn Dam, no young seen, still 4 on 20th December (IN)
S   Grangemouth – 530 on 9th March (DMB), still 65 on 27th April (DT);
       150 on 27th and 28th September (DMB,WRB)
SWP 1 pair at least on Lake of Menteith from 15th February (WRB,DT)
       Pairs at L. Watston (2Y) and L. Venachar (WRB)

*FULMAR
C   1 flying W along Craig Leith on 16th June (CJH)
S   4 over the Forth on 2nd September gained height and lost to sight
       high over Grangemouth (MWF,SKP)

*GANNET
S   Exhausted at Gargunnock on 19th March, died after 2 days (JG)
       Dead adult at Grangemouth on 14th September, one wing
       enmeshed in piece of net (DT)

CORMORANT
C/S Forth estuary, 325 on 19th December (DMB)
C   At Alloa "bridge", 73 on 15th January (PWS), only 10 on 30th
       August (CJH) but 102 on 21st September (DMB) and 90 on
       13th December (WRB)
S   Inland at Carron Valley Res. – 8 on 29th March, 7 on 16th and
       29th November (WRB,DT)
SWP 7 at Lake of Menteith on 13th January (JG), 5 at L. Watston on
       19th April (WRB)

*SHAG
S   1 at Skinflats on 21st December (DRW)

HERON
SWP 17 nests (13 with young) at Lake of Menteith on 19th April
       (WRB)

MUTE SWAN
C   Pair at Gartmorn Dam reared 6Y (IN), 10 at Cambus on 3rd
       December (DMB)
S   At Airthrey, 15 on 26th January, pair reared 7Y (MWF,CJH)
SWP Pairs at L. Watston (6Y), L. Lubnaig (failed), Muir Dam (WRB)

WHOOPER SWAN
Spring
C   50 (1 juv) on ley grass at Blairlogie through March, last 40 on
       4th April (CJH)
S   At Kippen/Gargunnock max. 40 on 23rd January (JG), present
       in much smaller numbers through February and March, last on
       13th April(JG,DT)
       At Airthrey 16 NW on 3rd and 11 NW on 6th April (MWF) –
       probably spring departure (Ed)
SWP 35 at Drip Moss on 19th January (JG,DT)

Autumn
C   18 (4 juv) on ley stubble at Menstrie on 8th November (CJH),
     max. 61 (12 juv) on 25th November (MAB)
S   4 at Arnprior on 8th October (DT). At Gargunnock 2 on
     25th October and 24 flying E on 8th November (JG). 30 near
     Skinflats end November — December (RD,DM). 42 at Stenhousemuir
     on 23rd December (DRM)
SWP At Drip Moss, 11 on flooded field on 26th November and 48 on
     17th December (JG). 39 at Thornhill on 3rd December, plus 1
     dead near a power line (JG). 58 at Lecropt on 10th December (PWS)

PINK-FOOTED GOOSE
C   80 E at Alva on 26th April (CJH). 250 SE at Muckhart on 20th
     September (DMB)
S   16 SW at Myot Hill (Denny) on 28th September (CJH). 300 SE
     at Cambuskenneth on 4th February (WRB). 450 at Kippen on
     29th March (WRB). 200 W at Stirling on 25th April (DRW)
SWP 1,000 near Lake of Menteith on 13th January (JG). 2,000
     Thornhill on 1st February (WRB). 1st of Autumn over Ashfield
     on 14th September (WRB). 65 SE at L. Lubnaig on 20th
     September (CJH). 1,000 over Doune on 2nd November (WRB)

*WHITE-FRONTED GOOSE
S   1 (European race) at Kippen on 29th March (WRB)

GREYLAG GOOSE
C   Only occasionally on ground by Forth, e.g. 62 at Tullibody Inch
     on 25th January (DMB). 150 at Cambus on 22nd March (CJH)
S   1 at Skinflats on 19th August (DMB). 1st flock 39 at Carron
     Valley Res. on 17th September (WRB)
SWP Pair and 6Y at L. Macanrie on 14th June (WRB). 2,000 near
     Gargunnock on 27th January, last 20 on 13th April (JG). 300
     at Lake of Menteith on 24th April (DT)

*CANADA GOOSE
S   3 NW at Airthrey on 27th May (MWF), possibly on moult
     movement (Ed)
SWP 1, with a Greylag, at Blairdrummond Moss on 26th March (JG),
     hybrids occur (Ed)

*BARNACLE GOOSE
S   2 with Greylags at Gargunnock on 24th February (JG)
SWP 1 at Flanders Moss on 11th October (MAB)

*BRENT GOOSE
S   1 feeding with Shelduck at Kinneil Sewage Works on 10th
     October (JG)

SHELDUCK
C   Inland, 2 at Gartmorn Dam on 20th May (IN)
S   9 pairs Dunmore-Fallin on 7 to 10th July (MWF). 1,272 at Skinflats
     on 20th January (DRW), Kinneil moult flock, 2,500 on 9th (ABM)
     and 2,158 on 10th August (DMB), 1,300 at Skinflats on 9th
     December, 2,710 on Forth estuary on 19th December (DMB)

WOOD DUCK
S   Male shot at Fallin on 2nd October (per DMB)

50 WIGEON

S   1st 5 at Skinflats on 16th August (DMB), 200 at Grangemouth on 27th January (WRB) often scarce inland of Stirling, e.g. in November 8 at Carron Valley Res. 4 at L. Coulter, 2 at Touch Res. 1 at North Third Res. (WRB,CJH,DT), 4 on Forth near Gargunnock on 17th February (JG)

SWP   2 Females at L. Mahaick on 2nd July (WRB), 10 at L. Watston on 31st August, max. only 18 at L. Venachar on 11th September (WRB)

*GADWALL

S   Male at Airthrey on 13th January and until 15th February (WRB,MWF,CJH)

TEAL

C   On Forth, 170 at Cambus on 27th January (CJH), 260 Tullibody Inch on 2nd February (WRB). At Gartmorn Dam 202 on 13th January, only 44 on 16th March (CJH,IN), 200 on 20th December (WRB). 200 on Devon floods (Dollar) on 28th December (RJY)

S   300 at Grangemouth on 15th January (DMB). Usually small numbers inland of Stirling but at Carron Valley Res. 93 on 19th January and 117 on 17th October (WRB)

SWP   1 or 2 pairs breeding season at Lake of Menteith, L. Macanrie, L. Watston, Muir Dam, L. Mahaick, Lochan Buidhe (WRB), 105 at Doune Ponds on 17th and 19th September (WRB)

MALLARD

C   At Gartmorn Dam, 1,300 on 2nd February, 1,295 on 28th September (WRB), 1,044 on 16th November (IN)

S   1,510 on Forth estuary on 20th January, 260 at Grangemouth on 31st January (DM) and 23rd August (DT). At Airthrey 312 on 26th January, only 10 on 9th March but 36 full grown on 26th June (suggesting influx to moult from elsewhere) (CJH). At Carron Valley Res. 218 on 19th January (WRB) and 341 on 29th November (DT). In November 350 at Touch Res. on 9th (CJH), 67 at North Third Res. and 55 at L. Coulter on 29th (DT)

SWP   At Lake of Menteith 196 on 13th January (JG) and 140 on 22nd November (DT), 360 at Castlehill Res. (new res. in Glendevon) on 22nd November (DMB), 250 at L. Watston on 31st August and 500 on 6th September, 100 at Doune Ponds on 19th September (WRB)

PINTAIL

S   59 at Skinflats on 30th January (DMB), 22 at Grangemouth on 28th January (MWF), 35 at Skinflats on 21st December (DRW)

C   3 at Tullibody Inch on 16th August (WRB)

*GARGANEY

SWP   Male at L. Watston on 31st August and 6th September (WRB)

SHOVELER

S   At Grangemouth, 16 on 4 dates 9th to 24th August (DMB,ABM)

C   1 at Craigie Pond on 21st September (WRB)

POCHARD

S   At Grangemouth, 49 on 20th January, 87 on 21st February (MWF,DT,DRW). 61 at Carron Valley Res. on 29th November (DT) otherwise scarce W of Stirling

C At Gartmorn Dam, 250 on 17th February, only 13 on 16th March, **51**
    400 on 21st September was quite exceptional, 144 on 14th December
    typical (WRB,CJH,IN). Few on Forth, max. 17 at Cambus on 27th
    January (CJH)
SWP 14 at L. Venachar on 12th January (WRB), 18 at L. Lubnaig on
    23rd January and 16 on 15th February (WRB,DT)

TUFTED DUCK
C Gartmorn Dam, 200 on 17th February (WRB), still 108 on 16th
    March (CJH,IN), only 22m and 12f seen in May, 4 broods noted (IN),
    89 on 16th June (IN) (suggests mid-summer influx, Ed), 250 on
    21st September (WRB), 138 on 16th November (IN). On Forth, 70
    at Cambus on 2nd February (CJH), 45 at Tullibody Inch on
    20th December (WRB)
S On Forth, 50 at Cambuskenneth on 4th February (WRB). At Airthrey
    144 on 30th January (MWF), few in February/March, 29 on 4th April,
    51 (26m) on 17th November (MWF), 4 pairs at Airthrey in May/June,
    1 duckling seen (CJH), pair Cocksburn Res. (WRB), 41 at Carron
    Valley Res. on 17th September (WRB) and 33 on 29th November (DT),
    32 at North Third Res. on 17th February (WRB), 21 on 1st March
    (AW), 24 on 14th December (DT)
SWP Duck + 4Y at Blairdrummond on 2nd July (WRB), 245 at Lake of
    Menteith on 13th January (JG), 26 at L. Watston on 1st September
    (WRB)

*SCAUP
S In Grangemouth area, 12 on 27th January (WRB) and 2 on 14th
    February (DRW), 6 on 24th and 8 on 27th September (DMB,DRW)

GOLDENEYE
C 62 (15m) at Gartmorn on 16th March, 64 on 14th December
    (CJH,IN). On Forth, 50 at Kennetpans on 15th January (DMB),
    60 at Cambus on 2nd February, still 33 on 22nd March (CJH), 28 on
    3rd December (DMB)
S On Forth, 88 flying E at Manorneuk on 19th January (CJH), 75 at
    Cambuskenneth on 4th February (WRB), 15 at L. Coulter on
    17th October, few on other waters (WRB)

*SMEW
S f/imm at Grangemouth on 24th August (DMB) (unusual date, Ed)
SWP f/imm at L. Venachar on 7th and 20th April (WRB,DT)

RED-BREASTED MERGANSER
S Grangemouth area, 115 on 20th and 350 on 27th January, 460 on
    6th February (DMB,WRB). 2 pairs at Earlsburn Res. 1 on 4th and
    1 pair at North Third Res. on 17th April (WRB,JG). 2 pairs Touch
    Res. on 23rd April, 4 birds on 15th June (WRB)
SWP at Lake of Menteith, 2 on 29th March (JG) and pair on 4th April (WRB)
    pair at L. Katrine (E) on 17th June (WRB)

GOOSANDER
C On Forth, 8 at Tullibody Inch on 25th January (DMB), 17(9m) at
    Cambus on 2nd February (CJH), 6 at Kinneil on 31st August (DMB) —
    early for estuary (Ed). On Devon, 4 at Dollar on 12th March (RY),
    8 at Muckhart 23rd November (DMB), 7 on Glendevon Res. on 30th
    November (CJH)
S 10(8m) at Cambuskenneth in February (CTJ). 17 at L. Laggan on 8th
    March (DT), 8(4m) at L. Coulter on 1st March (AW); 10 at North Third

Res. on 19th January and 6 on 7th September (WRB)

SWP 15 at Lake of Menteith on 13th January (JG). 7 at L. Katrine (E.) on 22nd April, 17 at L. Achray on 17th July (WRB), 17 at L. Venachar on 27th July (DT). Young seen at L. Lubnaig and Callander, probably other pairs Callander — Doune (WRB)

*HEN HARRIER

S 2 m over Gargunnock Hills on 4th April (JG), 1 at Pendreich Res. 19th September (CJH)

SWP 1 Aberfoyle on 4th April, m Callander on 31st August (WRB). m Torrie Forest on 20th September (CJH)

SPARROWHAWK

C Many records through year; mobbed by crows at Cambus on 22nd March and Alva on 20th September, mobbed by swallows at Cambus on 16th August (CJH)

S Regular through year at Gargunnock (JG), 1 over Stirling on 7th May (AW)

SWP Frequent Aberfoyle-Trossachs, 4 over Duke's Pass on 13th April (WRB), 3 pairs within ½ mile near Dunblane (4Y,2Y, eggs addled), probably another pair nearby (P.S—A)

BUZZARD

*C 1 over Alva mobbed by 2 Lesser Black-backed Gulls on 6th April (CJH)

*S 4 E at Airthrey on 13th February, 1 on 14th April (DMB)

SWP Frequent max 6 at Aberfoyle on 15th February and 7 at Braes of Doune on 1st March (WRB), 8 at Flanders Moss on 11th October (MWF,DH)

*ROUGH-LEGGED BUZZARD

SWP 1 at Sheriffmuir from 1st November to 13th December (E. Blake, DMB,MWF,DH)

GOLDEN EAGLE

SWP Several in Balquhidder — Callander hills (WRB,CJH), 1 at Sheriffmuir on 26th January, mobbed by a smaller raptor (Miss E. Lapthorn)

OSPREY

S 1 mobbed by gulls over Stirling on 2nd May (DRW)

KESTREL

S Pair with nest on pylon at South Alloa on 11th July (MWF). Nest with young at Ballochleam on 4th July (WRB)

SWP Nest with young at Callander on 29th July (WRB). Max 4 at Sheriffmuir on 6th December (MWF,DH)

MERLIN

*C 1 at Muckhart on 4th October (DMB)

*S 1 at Dumyat on 27th September, chasing small passeres (CM), 1 at Kippen on 9th October (DK), 1 at Blairlogie on 18th November (MAB), 1 at Cambuskenneth in late December (KPA). Grangemouth area 5 on 20th January to 21st February (WRB, MWF,DT,DRW), seen to catch a Dunlin.

PEREGRINE

Breeding 2Y reared at site in W of area, immature pair at another site. In E of area 2Y (m and f) reared at a site where no breeding has been attempted for ten years, first seen 5th April, last on 24th August.

C   1 over Alva on 14th January, 20th September (CJH)   **53**
S   Grangemouth area, 1 on 20th and 28th January (MWF,DRW),
1 on 24th August (DMB), 1 at North Third Res. on 19th January
and 15th November (WRB).

PARTRIDGE
S   Near Gargunnock max of 22 in January and 9 in November (JG).
12 on Stirling University lawns on 12th November (MWF)
SWP   10 at Barbush on 9th August (WRB)

*QUAIL
SWP   1 at Easter Row (Doune) on 26th June (MAB)

*WATER RAIL
SWP   1 calling at L. Ruskie on 30th June (WRB)

*CORNCRAKE
S   1 calling through June at Gargunnock (JG)
SWP   2 calling at Drip Moss on 28th June (WRB). 1 in uncut hay at
Lake of Menteith on 14th June (JM)

MOORHEN
C   6 on Gartmorn Dam 20th May (IN) (?4—5 pairs, Ed)
S   1 pair breeding at Airthrey although max 8 on 15th February
and 17th November (MWF,CJH)
SWP   3 pairs bred at Doune Ponds (WRB)

COOT
C   20+ pairs at Gartmorn Dam (CJH,IN) 138 on 14th and 125 on
28th September (WRB,CJH,IN)
S   At Airthrey Loch, 55 on 26th January, 60 on 4th February
down to 33 on 4th April (WRB,MWF), ca 15 pairs nested,
7 to 10 broods hatched   (CJH), 22 on 17th November (MWF)
SWP   Lake of Menteith, 359 on 13th January (JG) and 120 on 29th
November (WRB). Pair bred (2Y) at Doune Ponds (WRB)

OYSTERCATCHER
Spring arrival, mainly calling at night : C. Alva on 15th February, 40 on
pasture at Cambus on 22nd March (CJH). S. over Stirling on 9th and
13th February, (DT,DRW), Airthrey on 16th February (MWF), 85 at
Cambuskenneth on 16th February (DT), 4 at Gargunnock on 24th
February (JG), 3 at L. Coulter on 1st March (AW). SWP. over Dunblane
on 22nd February (PSA)
S   up to 4 over Stirling on 7th, 29th and 30th May (AW). 24
over Gargunnock on 24th August (JG), 1 E at Airthrey on
12th November (MWF) (unusual inland after late summer, Ed)
SWP   72 Ashfield on 29th March, 30 at Barbush on 9th August
(WRB). 2 pairs at Doune Ponds c/3 at Kilbryde (WRB)

RINGED PLOVER
S   Grangemouth area, 183 on 11th and 70 on 18th May, 95 on
10th August. 264 on Forth estuary on 16th August (DMB)
2 pairs displaying at Earlsburn Res. on 4th April (JG)
SWP   Seen Doune Ponds on 10th April, 2 pairs reared young
(WRB,PWS). Pair at Blairdrummond on 14th August (WRB)

GOLDEN PLOVER
C   30 on pasture at Cambus on 22nd March (CJH)
S   5 at Skinflats on 2nd July and 120 on 4th July (MWF),
1,000 at Kinneil on 27th September (DMB), 1,250 on Forth

estuary on 21st December (DMB)
Visible movement : 5 S at Denny Ridge on 11th and 7 SW
on 27th September. 26 SSW at Myot Hill and 8 SSW at
North Third Res. on 28th September (CJH)

SWP 2 displaying at Meall Odhar (Callander) on 1st March (WRB)

GREY PLOVER

S Grangemouth area, 39 on 25th January, 1st of autumn 2 on
28th July rising to 40 on 27th September (DMB,DT)

LAPWING

C Displaying over fields at Menstrie on 10th March, still flock
of 90 at Cambus on 22nd March (snow) (CJH). Few on
inland fields in late summer; 690 in an hour flying downstream
at Cambus on 16th August; return in early autumn, e.g. 740
on ley grass at Menstrie on 27th September (CJH)

S Many pairs around Gargunnock (JG), return to Carse round
Kippen from 12th February (WRB); however, still 1,180 at
Skinflats on 14th February (DRW); 300 at L. Coulter on
1st March (AW); 165 at Skinflats as early as 2nd July (MWF);
3,000 at Bandeath on 16th August (WRB); 400 at Camelon
on 13th October (AW)

SWP Inland return 11th to 15th February. 500 at Ashfield on 2nd
August (WRB). 60 flying S, very high, at L. Lubnaig on 18th
October (CJH)

KNOT

S At Kinneil, 1,500 on 6th February and 5,560 on 9th December
(DMB)

SANDERLING

S 1 at Skinflats on 11th May; 4 at Kinneil on 20th July and 1 on
10th August (DMB)

LITTLE STINT

S Grangemouth area, 2 on 23rd August, 1 on 13th, 4 on 24th and
2 on 27th September (DMB,DT,DRW)

CURLEW SANDPIPER

S Grangemouth area, 26 bird-days 24th August to 28th September,
max. 8 on 13th September (DMB,DT)

DUNLIN

S 2,640 at Skinflats 11th February (DRW), 900 at Kinneil on 20th
January (DT) and 500 on 28th September (WRB). Green dyed
birds seen in February (DRW)

SWP 3 at L. Macanrie on 14th June (WRB)

RUFF

C 8 at Tullibody Inch on 16th August and 14 on 30th August
(CJH,WRB). 4 at Craigie Pond on 16th August (WRB)

S Grangemouth area, 42 bird-days 10th August to 27th September,
max. 18 on 31st August and 13 on 27th September (DMB,DT)

SWP At Barbush, m and f on 14th and 2 m on 15th August (WRB)

SNIPE

Only small numbers recorded.

C 6 at marshy spring at Alva on 3rd February, snow and frost
(CJH)

S   Only seen twice at Gargunnock in January and August (JG)
SWP Displaying at 380m on Ben an't Sithein on 9th April (WRB), 4 at Doune Ponds on 17th September (WRB)

WOODCOCK
C   2 roding at Wood Hill on 2nd March (CJH)
SWP Roding at Dunblane on 1st and 2nd March (PSA), Ashfield on 7th April, (WRB)

*BLACK-TAILED GODWIT
S   At Kinneil, 1 on 4th and 11th, 2 on 6th and 17th February, 1 on 13th, 14th, 24th and 27th September (DMB,DT,DP)

*BAR-TAILED GODWIT
S   180 at Kinneil on 7th September (DMB), 181 on 7th February (DRW)

WHIMBREL
S   Grangemouth area, 19 bird-days from 10th July to 31st August, max. 10 on 20th July (DMB,WRB,MWF,SKP,DT)

CURLEW
S   Grangemouth area, 280 on 17th February, still 45 on 27th April (DT). 360 on 4th July (MWF), 330 on 13th September (DMB). Inland return to Gargunnock on 17th February (JG), L. Coulter on 1st March (AW), 62 near Gargunnock after snow on 21st March (JG)
SWP Inland return above Callander on 1st March (WRB)

SPOTTED REDSHANK
S   Grangemouth area, 1 on 14th August, 2 on 27th September, 2 on 9th December (DMB)

REDSHANK
S   910 at Skinflats on 25th January (DMB), still 170 on 27th April (DT). Inland return to Gargunnock on 23rd March (JG). 740 at Skinflats on 21st December (DRW)
SWP Return to Ashfield on 11th February (WRB)

GREENSHANK
C   At Cambus, 1 on 2nd and 16th August (WRB,CJH)
S   Grangemouth area, 77 bird-days 1st July (early) to 27th September, mainly early August to mid September, max. 10 on 31st August (DMB,DT,ABM). Also 1 on 11th May (DMB). 1 on 14th and 28th January (MWF,DM) and 30th December (DMB)
SWP 1 at Barbush 9th and 16th August, 1 at Doune Ponds on 17th to 19th September (WRB)

GREEN SANDPIPER
SWP 1 at Barbush on 15th and 16th August (WRB), 1 nearby on 24th August (E. Blake)

COMMON SANDPIPER
S   1 at Airthrey on 4th and 2 at Stirling on 9th April (MWF). Grangemouth area, from 28th July to 27th September, max. 8 on 31st August (DMB,WRB)
SWP Spring return to Teith 23rd to 24th April (WRB,DT). Possibly bred Doune Ponds (WRB)

56 ARCTIC SKUA
  S   Grangemouth area, 5 on 24th August, 2 on 21st September
  (DMB). 1 over Cambuskenneth on 14th October (KPA)

POMARINE SKUA
  S   Grangemouth area, 1 on 31st January (DMB)

BLACKHEADED GULL
  S   20 pairs Carron Valley Res. low water — probably not
  successful (WRB)
  SWP 250 pairs at Muir Dam on 19th April, 150 pairs at
  Blairdrummond GP (30 nests seen) on 2nd July, 25 pairs
  at Ashfield marsh — 15 + young reared (WRB)

COMMON GULL
  S   10 pairs on islet on west L. Katrine. 2,000 at roost on
  L. Coulter on 17th September — regular sunset flightline
  SSW over Stirling (WRB)
  SWP 10 pairs reared 10 Y at Blairdrummond. Pair prospected
  Ashfield (WRB)

LESSER BLACK-BACKED GULL
  S   Late bird at Stirling on 9th November (MWF). Spring arrival: 1 at
  Stirling on 17th and 1 at Ballochleam on 21st February (DT)
  SWP 17 at Thornhill on 15th February, 2,000 at Lake of Menteith
  by 6th April. Colony at East Flanders Moss numbering
  thousands (WRB)

HERRING GULL
  S   1,500 at Cambuskenneth on 4th February (WRB)
  SWP 500 pairs at East Flanders Moss on 4th July (WRB). (A tenfold
  increase since 1974, Ed)

HYBRID GULL
  1 adult at Kinneil on 7th February, larger than nearby Herring
  Gulls, white wing tips but lacking heavy bill of typical Glaucous
  Gull, possibly Glaucous/Herring hybrid (DRW). Probably the same
  bird was seen on 20th January and 6th February (DMB,DT)

GREATER BLACK-BACKED GULL
  C   47 at Alloa on 30th August (CJH)

KITTIWAKE
  S   100 off Bo'ness on 30th and 31st January (DMB)
  (District)

SANDWICH TERN
  S   Grangemouth area, max. 100 on 24th August, last 1 on 27th
  September (DMB). 2 flying W over Gargunnock on 4th August
  (D. Holmes)

BLACK TERN
  S   1 at Kinneil on 14th September, possibly flew inland (DT)

COMMON TERN
  S   At Grangemouth, 20 on 27th April, 56 nests on 24th May,
  36 + Y reared (DMB)

GUILLEMOT
  C   1 at Kennetpans on 30th January
  S   1, oiled but alive, at Grangemouth on 24th and 25th January

(MWF). 1 at Skinflats on 21st December (DRW)   **57**

STOCK DOVE
C   5 pairs at South Alloa railway "bridge" on 16th July (MWF)
S   Pair breeding in quarry above Gargunnock (JG). 25 at Skinflats
    on 27th January (WRB). 20 at Airthrey on 30th October (DMB)
SWP In west, 3 at Kinlochard on 26th January, pair investigating
    Creag Dubh on 15th February (WRB)

WOODPIGEON
SWP 1,000 at Doune Ponds on 2nd November (WRB)

*COLLARED DOVE
C   Decrease in occupied area in Alva. At Menstrie pair seen from
    2nd August to end of year, 1st known record (CJH)
S   Now very common at Gargunnock, up to 25 in November (JG).
    Pair made a partly wire nest 16m up a crane in use at Stirling,
    c/2 hatched 9th June, 1 young died and adults deserted by
    13th June (AW)
SWP Generally few noted (WRB). (A village by village account of the
    distribution of this species would be very valuable (Ed))

CUCKOO
S   1st at Gargunnock on 11th May (JG)
SWP Heard Brig o'Turk, L. Lubnaig, Callander (WRB)

TAWNY OWL
S   At Kippen one killed a fledged Collared Dove on nest,
    adults present, dropped it fatally wounded (DK). None heard
    at Gargunnock this year (JG)
SWP 1 hunting from power line at Blairdrummond Moss on 28th
    June (WRB)

*LONG-EARED OWL
S   1 at Sauchie Crags on 17th April (WRB). 1 dead (? poison) at
    Leckie Res. on 26th August (JG)

*SHORT-EARED OWL
S   Pair near Fintry on 30th March (PWS). 1 at Kinneil on 20th
    January (DT)
SWP 1 at L. Mahaick on 6th August (WRB). 1 over peat hags at
    Lag a Phuill (Balquhidder) on 7th December (CJH). This
    species remains remarkably scarce.

SWIFT
First records: (C) : 3 at Muckhart on 11th May. (S) : 3 at Stirling
and 1 at Airthrey on 8th May (CJH,AW). (SWP) : 3 at Callander on
11th May (DT).
Last records: (C) : 1 at Alva on 23rd August (CJH). (S) : 20 at
Stirling on 15th August. (SWP) : 1 at Ashfield on 13th August
(WRB)
C   300 W in 2 hours at Kincardine Bridge on 3rd July (MWF). 45
    apparently taking swarming ants over Alva on 25th July (CJH)
SWP 200 at Lake of Menteith on 14th June (WRB)

KINGFISHER
C   1 on Devon, Crook of Devon stretch, 25th July and 14th to
    30th November (DMB,RY)
S   1 at Airthrey Loch on 10th January, 11th February, 3rd

and 13th April, 12th and 13th November (DMB,WRB,DH,MWF).
1 at Kippen in late summer (DK)
These records suggest a few breeding pairs (Ed)

GREEN WOODPECKER
S &   Juveniles seen Aberfoyle, Kilmahog, Polmaise (WRB). Regular
SWP   Doune, records from 12 other localities between Carron Valley
and Trossachs (many observers).

GREAT SPOTTED WOODPECKER
C   No proved breeding, 1 by Black Devon near Forestmill on 23rd
February (CJH). 1 drumming at Alloa on 7th March — have
been coming for peanuts for several years (Miss I. Whyte)
S   In summer at Gargunnock, Bridge of Allan and Castlecary,
winter at Fintry and Polmaise (JG,WRB,DRW)
SWP   Spring/summer records at L. Ard, Trossachs, Aberfoyle, Lanrick,
Doune (WRB)

SKYLARK
C   300 in sheep feeding field at Cambus on 22nd March, 200 on
grass stubble at Alva on 23rd March, snowy spell (CJH). 100
at Craigie Pond on 21st September (WRB)
S   200 SE at Cambuskenneth on 4th February (WRB). Very
numerous on fields around Plean on 27th September. Small
movements between WSW and ESE in Bridge of Allan area
19th September to 10th October, surprisingly scarce in
passerine flights over Denny Ridge and Myot Hill (CJH)
SWP   1st song at Ashfield on 11th February, 1 on Stuc a Chroin
at 830m on 1st March (WRB). Many on fields at Lecropt
on 30th September, a few flying between SSE and SW
at Torrie Forest on 20th September and 41 W to
SSW over Braes of Doune on 4th October (CJH)

SANDMARTIN
C   20 at Dollar on 15th April (DMB)
SWP   2 at Cambusmore (Callander) on 6th and 4 at Lake of Menteith
on 7th with 150 on 19th April. 60 at Barbush on 17th April,
last 10 on 8th September (WRB)

SWALLOW
C   2 at Dollar on 15th April, last at Muckhart on 18th October
(DMB)
S   Last at Gargunnocks on 7th and at Carron Valley Res. on 17th
October (JG,WRB). 1 at Bridge of Allan on 6th November (DT).
Most directions of apparent migration are inconsistent, however
16 in 4 groups to SW and S over main ridge of Gargunnock
on 31st August (CJH)
SWP   1st at Port of Menteith and Dunblane on 9th, Callander on 14th
and Doune on 15th April (WRB,MWF,SKP, K. Graham). A late
nest at Dunblane had large young on 7th September (PSA)

HOUSEMARTIN
C   3 at Dollar on 16th April (DMB) not at Alva until 4th May (CJH).
Relatively few at Alva in early autumn. 200 at Muckhart on 9th
September.
S   1st at Gargunnock on 1st May (JG). 100 at Stirling on 10th and
65 at Airthrey on 25th September (WRB,CJH)

SWP 10 pairs at Ashfield, feeding 2nd broods until 15th September.   **59**
40 feeding whilst perched on sallow bushes at Doune on 20th
September (WRB) (of report for 1977, Ed)

TREE PIPIT
S   Last 1 over Stirling on 29th August (WRB)
SWP 1st at Callander on 14th April (WRB)

MEADOW PIPIT
C   50 on frozen, flooded pasture at Cambus on 27th January —
large group for winter (CJH)
S   Many parties flying mainly between W and SE at Bridge of Allan,
Gargunnock Hills, Denny Ridge, Myot Hill, Plean and Slamannan,
31st August — 2nd October, max. 84 in 1 hour on 19th September
(CJH)
SWP 100 on moors near Tighnablair on 9th September (largest autumn
party) (CJH). Many parties flying between W and SE at Lecropt,
Braes of Doune, Torrie Forest, L. Lubnaig and Glen Ogle, 9th
September to 4th October (CJH)

*ROCK PIPIT
S   Grangemouth area, 1 on 20th January, 2 on 21st December (DRW)

YELLOW WAGTAIL
S   Male at Kinneil on 28th July (WRB)

GREY WAGTAIL
C/S More late autumn and winter records than usual, up to 3 in
November at Crook of Devon (DMB), 7 roosting in willows at
Airthrey on 14th November (MWF). In January, February and
December at Gartmorn Dam, Alva, Grangemouth, Airthrey,
Bridge of Allan (WRB,CJH,SM,AW). Movements: 2 SW at Muckhart
on 27th September, 1 SE Pendreich 19th September, 2 S at
Ballochleam on 31st August (DMB,CJH)

PIED WAGTAIL
C   Roost in reeds at Cambus in November, max. 56 on 22nd
November, only 6 on 19th December (MWF,CJH)
S   Male White Wagtail with Pieds at Airthrey on 13th to 16th
August (MWF)
SWP Max. at Ashfield, 15 on 17th August. Roost of 60 at L. Watston
on 1st September (WRB). 5 S at L. Lubnaig on 20th September
(CJH)

DIPPER
C   Singing at Dollar and Forestmill in late February (CJH,RJY).
Up to 18 in November on Devon between Glendevon and Crook
of Devon (DMB)
SWP 3 or 4 pairs Ashfield — Kippenrosss, 2 pairs Leny Falls, feeding
young on 20th April (WRB)

WREN
S/   Some improvement in numbers this year (WRB). Good year in
SWP CBC at Falkirk (AMcI)

DUNNOCK
C   1st song on 13th February at Dollar (RJY)
SWP 1st song at Dunblane on 24th February (ABM)

60 ROBIN

S   Autumn song often heard at night at Airthrey, max. 7 at 02.00 (bright moon) on 20th December (MWF). Good year in CBC plot at Falkirk (AMcl)

REDSTART

C   1 in gorse at Alva on 24th August, presumably migrant (CJH). No other records.

S   Male at Ballochleam on 22nd June (WRB). 1 in garden at Gargunnock on 3rd September (JG).

SWP   Widespread in breeding season, 1st at L. Ard on 16th Brig o'Turk and Port of Menteith on 20th April (WRB). 6 singing Trossachs-Brenachoile on 22nd April, male at Blairdrummond 2nd July, pair Kippenross 4th June (WRB). 35 pairs in boxes at L. Katrine (H. Robb)

*STONECHAT

C   Pair in Alva gorse 25th May to 24th August, at least 2 Y reared (CJH)

SWP   Pair with young near Braco on 9th June (PWS), 2 immature in Menteith Hills on 9th July (DT)

WHEATEAR

C   Juveniles on Craig Leith by 15th June (CJH). Last 1 at Tullibody Inch on 4th October (ABM)

S   1st at Gargunnock on 4th April (JG). 3 pairs Touch Res. (WRB). Early migrant at Skinflats on 4th July (MWF)

SWP   6 at Inverlochlarig on 6th April, 2 at Ashfield on 15th September — 1 resembled the large Greenland type (WRB)

BLACKBIRD

S   1st song at Stirling on 11th February (WRB)

FIELDFARE

S   240 at Bandeath on 2nd February (WRB). !st of autumn, 15 at Airthrey on 4th October (WRB), widespread 11th to 19th October (DMB,JG,CJH,ABM,AW). 800 to W and SW over Gargunnock on 19th October (JG), 200 at Shieldhill on 11th November (AW)

SWP   200 at Lecropt on 19th October (ABM), 25 NW up Kirkton Glen on 16th October (WRB). There is at the moment no evidence of any southerly movement in the Balquhidder-Strathyre area (Ed)

SONG THRUSH

C   Frequent song around Dollar on 26th January (RJY)

C/S/
SWP   As usual, noticeably scarce in January and early February (WRB,CJH), returned to Ashfield on 11th February (WRB)

S   3 flew off high to W from Stirling Castle on 24th September (CJH)

REDWING

C   During snow on 3rd February at Alva several parties frequented open leafy places under trees. 1st of autumn, 25 at Tillicoultry on 4th October (CJH)

S   Several parties S at Stirling on 2nd to 4th February, otherwise scarce in winter (WRB). 1st of autumn at Stirling on 4th October (DRW). 200 flying between SW and W at Gargunnock

on 19th October (JG)
SWP   1st of autumn, 1 at Dunblane on 24th September (WRB)

MISTLE THRUSH
C   few in midwinter (CJH). Completed nest at Dollar on 10th March (RJY)
S   Fairly common in small numbers through year at Gargunnock (JG). 14 at Airthrey on 6th September (CJH)
SWP   50 at Cromlix on 8th September (WRB). 5 S at Lecropt on 30th September (CJH)

*GRASSHOPPER WARBLER
C   1 singing by Devon at Dollar on 11th July (Mrs. E. A. Greenfield)
S   Presumed migrant(s) singing at Airthrey on 20th and 22nd April and 6th May (MWF,CJH,DRW)
SWP   3 singing at Drip Moss on 28th June, 1 at L. Dhu on 1st July, alarm calls at Kingshouse on 19th June and Inverlochlarig on 25th July (WRB)

SEDGE WARBLER
C   3 singing on Alloa Inch on 7th July (MWF)
S   1st at Airthrey on 25th April, last on 2nd October (MWF)
SWP   5 pairs on Allan Water, Kinbuck-Barbush, in June. 2 pairs at Inverlochlarig (WRB) — shows extreme penetration of a highland glen (Ed)

WHITETHROAT
S   1st at Gargunnock on 11th May (JG)
SWP   3 pairs at Doune Ponds, generally widespread along southern margin of hill ground (WRB)

GARDEN WARBLER
S   Singing at Airthrey on 18th May (MWF)
SWP   Singing at Brig o'Turk on 17th May (DT). 2 pairs at Doune Ponds (WRB)

BLACKCAP
S   Singing at Airthrey on 16th April (MWF). 2 pairs Gargunnock (JG). Male at Bridge of Allan on 31st December.
SWP   Apparently scarce (Ed). Present Trossachs, Doune (WRB)

WOOD WARBLER
S   1st at Bridge of Allan on 14th April (DRW)
SWP   1st at L. Ard on 8th May (DT). Widespread and locally frequent in west, e.g. deciduous woods of L. Ard Forest (Stirling SOC), east L. Katrine, Trossachs, Brig o'Turk (WRB)

CHIFF CHAFF
S   1st at Airthrey on 27th March (MWF,SKP). A phylloscopus at Cambuskenneth on 14th December was probably this species (KPA)
SWP   Singing at Dunblane on 3rd April, present in 5 localities Dunblane-Callander (WRB,DT,PWS)

WILLOW WARBLER
C   1st at Muckhart on 15th April (DMB), big arrival along Hillfoots on 17th April (CJH)
S   2 at Airthrey on 12th April (DRW)
SWP   Widespread Doune-Aberfoyle on 13th April, last 3 at Doune Ponds on 3rd September (WRB)

62 GOLDCREST
SWP   Altitude distribution, up to 450m in Kirkton Glen plantations (WRB)

*PIED FLYCATCHER
SWP   38 pairs in nest boxes at L. Katrine (H. Robb) Male and immature at Strathyre on 6th July (WRB)

LONG-TAILED TIT
C   Parties (max. 11) all along Blackdevon, Gartmorn-Forestmill, on 23rd February, 14 in willow/birch scrub at Tillicoultry on 23rd June (CJH)
SWP   Small flocks widespread (WRB). Young flew at Dunblane on 22nd/23rd May (PSA), 25 at L. Lubnaig on 20th September (CJH)

COAL TIT
SWP   Max. flock, 20 at Callander on 10th December (WRB)

BLUE TIT
C   Brood hatched 19th May, fledged 5th June near Kincardine (DM)
S   Nest building at Airthrey on 15th March (MWF), 42 in reeds at Cambus on 22nd November (MWF)

GREAT TIT
S   Singing at Airthrey on 22nd January (CJH)
SWP   Singing at Kinlochard on 26th January, 40 at Callander on 10th December (WRB)

GREAT GREY SHRIKE
C   1 at Menstrie on 5th March (PL)
SWP   1 at Duke's Pass, Aberfoyle, 4th to 12th April (WRB)

JAY
*C   1 at Forestmill on 23rd February (CJH)
S   1 at Pendreich on 7th November (ABM), 2 at Gargunnock mid September — early November (JG), 1 at Airthrey on 27th April (DRW). As usual, few non-breeding season records for south-east of area (Ed)

MAGPIE
S   Regular at Gargunnock, max. 5 on 18th March (JG). Maintaining status around Falkirk, max. roost flock of 12 (AMcl)
SWP   Present at Dunblane, Gartmore-Aberfoyle (WRB)

ROOK
C   Rookeries, 195 nests at Menstrie on 12th April, little change (CJH), 220 + at Gartmorn on 19th April (increase of 65 over 1978) (CJH)
S   Flocks of up to 100 taking acorns at Airthrey 13th to 29th October (DMB,CJH)
SWP   1 hung upside down for several seconds from a power line at Doune on 22nd January (WRB)

CARRION CROW
C   Max. 20 roosting at Wood Hill on 21st December (CJH) — flocks greatly reduced since early and mid 1970's.

HOODED CROW
SWP   Several, with rather dirty looking plumage, in mixed pairs with Carrion Crows south of Balquhidder on 7th December (CJH)

RAVEN   63

S   3 on sheep carcase at Gargunnock Hill on 14th April (JG), 3 at Sheriffmuir on 13th December (DMB)

SWP 7 at Uamh Beg on 31st August (WRB), present Glen Dubh (CJH), Ben Vane, Ben an't sithein, L. Venachar (WRB)

STARLING

C   Nested near Kincardine in holes used by Swifts in 1979 (DM)

S   Dusk flights (roosting) to the west over Airthrey in late autumn (CJH)

SWP Roost of 4,000 at Keir Ptn. in September-October (WRB)

HOUSE SPARROW

C   40 near Cambus on 16th August (CJH)

S   90 at Shieldhill on 9th September (AW)

TREE SPARROW

SWP 4 at Doune on 12th January (WRB). Seems very scarce in Stirling and Clack. Districts (Ed)

CHAFFINCH

C   Winter flocks small, e.g. 50 at Gartmorn on 14th January, 77 round sheep troughs at Alva on 3rd February (CJH)

S   Singing at Airthrey on 11th February (DRW), 170 at Airthrey on 11th February (WRB)

SWP Singing at L. Ard. on 26th and Ashfield on 30th January, 200 at Doune on 15th January and 150 on 22nd December, 100 at W Dullater on 29th February (WRB)

Autumn movement C/S/SWP : small visible migration flights widespread 11th September to 15th October, max. 45 per hour at Cult Hill on 14th September, mainly between SW and S but a few to E over Bridge of Allan (CJH)

BRAMBLING

C   2 in finch flock on stubble at Alva on 23rd March (CJH)

S   2 singles in February, 1st of autumn at Pendreich on 28th September, 18 at L. Coulter on 13th December, 10 at North Third Res. on 16th and 10 at Buchlyvie on 21st December (WRB)

GREENFINCH

C   60 in stubble at Alva on 23rd March (CJH)

GOLDFINCH

C   25 at Muckhart on 14th November (DMB)

S   60 by Wharry Burn on 9th and 60 on thistles at Pendreich on 19th September (CJH), 8 there on 7th November flew with Fieldfares (ABM). Small numbers through year at Gargunnock (JG)

SWP Nest found near Dunblane (WRB)

SISKIN

C   20 at Muckhart on 3rd October (DMB)

S   30 at Airthrey on 15th April (MWF), 50 in scrub rowans at Ballochleam on 31st August (CJH), 12 in cypresses in Bridge of Allan on 16th November (ABM)

SWP 2 pairs at peanuts at Dunblane on 29th January (Miss E. Lapthorn). Many in Drummore Wood (L. Ard Forest) on 31st May (Stirling SOC), 20 in that area on 7th November (PWS), 15 at Glen Finglass on 30th August, 60 at Strathyre on 26th November (WRB)

LINNET

C   100 at Craigie on 21st September (WRB), 100 at Kennetpans on 21st November (MWF)

S   110 at Shieldhall on 30th September (AW)

REDPOLL

C   Several calling near Devon at Tillicoultry on 23rd June, 3 in garden at Alva on 16th August (CJH)

SWP   10 Callander Crags on 10th January (WRB),(seem scarcer this year Ed)

TWITE

C   35 at Blackdevonmouth on 27th January, 50 in weeds at Cambus on 2nd February, only 5 there on 22nd March (CJH)

S   Grangemouth area, 75 on 20th January (DT), 43 on 5th February (MWF)

SWP   50 at Drip Moss on 24th January (MAB) — very few inland records in winter (Ed)

CROSSBILL

S   1 at Airthrey on 11th February, 10 at Polmaise on 27th November (WRB), 13 near Buchlyvie on 30th March (R. G. Caldow), 3 (1 male, 1 juvenile) in oaks in L. Ard Forest on 31st May (Stirling SOC)

SWP   Evidence of breeding at Gartmore and two sites near Aberfoyle (WRB)

BULLFINCH

C   7 deep in conifer plantations at Forestmill in December (CJH)

S   20, 12 and 12 at Sauchie Crags on 26th January (E. Barth). Frequent around Gargunnock, bred, max. 8 on 7th February (JG)

SWP   30 at Callander Crags on 8th January (WRB)

HAWFINCH

S   2 at Bridge of Allan on 2nd May (MAB)

SWP   1 at Dunblane on 16th November (PSA)

SNOW BUNTING

S   20 on stubble at Cambuskenneth on 30th January (GTJ), 80 at Kippen Muir on 12th November (WRB)

YELLOWHAMMER

C   15 at Gartmorn Dam on 14th January, 23 in stubble at Menstrie on 22nd March (CJH)

SWP   17 at Doune Ponds on 12th January, 3 pairs bred. Singing in Glen Buckie on 3rd March (WRB)

REED BUNTING

C   4 singing on Alloa Inch on 7th July, 50 roosting in reeds at Cambus on 22nd November (MWF)

S   2 pairs bred at Airthrey (MWF). Regular by Forth at Gargunnock (J. Gearing)

SWP   In summer widespread but not numerous Doune-Callander (WRB)

CORN BUNTING   **65**
    C   The 1979 albino seen near Menstrie on 16th August (CJH)
    S   3 singing at Skinflats on 28th July (WRB)
    SWP Singing at Cambusdrenny on 28th June (WRB)

The following observers are referred to by initials in the report:

K. P. Anderson, M. A. Brazil, D. M. Bryant, W. R. Brackenridge,
M. W. Fraser, J. Gearing, C. J. Henty, D. Hickson, G. T. Jamieson,
D. Kerridge, Mrs. P. Lee, A. MacIver, C. McLeod, D. Matthews,
A. B. Mitchell, J. Mitchell, I. Nicoll, Miss S. K. Penner,
P. W. Sandeman, P. Stirling-Aird, D. Thorogood, D. R. Waugh,
A. Wood, R. J. Young.

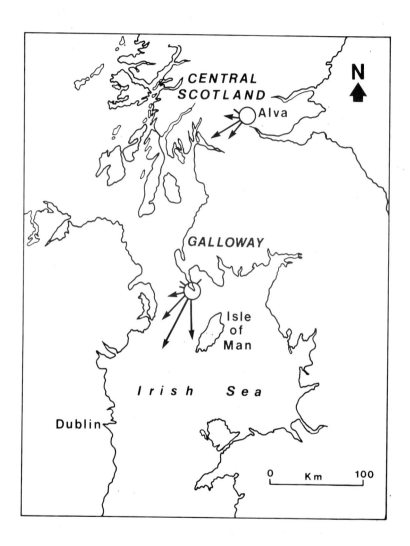

Figure 1   Directions of flight of nocturnal migrants in autumn over central and south-west Scotland. The lengths of the arrows correspond to the numbers in Table 1.

NOCTURNAL MIGRATION IN SOUTHWEST AND CENTRAL SCOTLAND DETECTED BY MOONWATCHING

C. J. Henty
University of Stirling

In October 1978 the numbers of night migrants seen crossing the face of the moon were greater than in previous years described in an earlier study (Henty 1978) and I was luckily able to compare results from central Scotland and Galloway. The new data confirm and extend conclusions about the identity and destination of birds flying over central Scotland, the influence of wind direction and the occurrence of calls given in flight.

METHODS

Observations were made with x20 binoculars during clear spells in the evening between 18.25 and 22.25 GMT. On October 12 and 18 I was at Alva, Clackmannanshire, the site of earlier work, just south of

68 the Ochil hills; on October 13, 15 and 17 I was on the coast 180 km to the south west near the tip of the Mull of Galloway. The techniques of observation and treatment of data are as described previously (Henty *loc. cit.*) and, in addition, attention was paid at the Mull of Galloway to birds seen during the day.

NUMBERS AND SPECIES REPRESENTED

The numerical results are presented in Table 1. As in previous years there is great variation from night to night which is not simply connected with local weather. Thus calm conditions or light winds are in general the circumstances under which large migratory flights are started and the strongest passage (on the 17th, the biggest I have ever seen) occurred in Galloway with a light north wind; however there was negligible passage the next evening with calm conditions inland. Conversely the strong movement inland into a moderate wind on the 12th was followed the next evening by negligible results on the coast during light winds, whilst at the latter site on the 15th a strong passage occurred with force five winds. The important conclusions are that passages of similar intensity can be seen inland in central Scotland and on the coast in Galloway and may occur with quite strong following winds or moderate contrary winds. That many birds may fly into moderate headwinds was also noted in the earlier study.

At the Mull of Galloway many Redwings (*Turdus iliacus*) were both heard at night and seen during the day whilst variation in numbers from day to day suggested considerable passage of Skylarks (*Alauda arvensis*), Song Thrushes (*T. philomenos*), Blackbirds (*T. merula*), Robins (*Erithacus rubecula*), Goldcrests (*R. regulus*) and Wrens (*T. troglodytes*). A few Song Thrushes and Skylarks were heard overhead at night as were single Golden Plover (*Pluvialis apricaria*) and Grey Goose (*Anser sp.*). Extra but imprecise data came on October 15 when there was thin cloud in front of the moon and fifteen birds were seen briefly against this background, most of these were flying between south and west.

DIRECTIONS OF FLIGHT

Inland in Clackmannanshire the direction of movement across the moon was mainly to the WSW, as in previous years. On the coast the direction on the two best nights was much more toward the SSW and S rather than WSW (Figure 1).

Since the winds were northerly this SSW direction of flight is probably due to lateral drift induced by the wind, an effect also suspected at Alva in 1976, although the possibility of birds with a particular preferred direction choosing particular winds cannot be entirely discounted. Lack (1969) concluded from radar studies that, although most variations in track direction were not due to crosswinds, there were occasional passages where the birds were drifted laterally by strong winds, this could occur in both spring and autumn and for day as well as night migrants.

IMPLICATIONS OF THE OBSERVED DIRECTIONS OF FLIGHT

Birds flying WSW over the Mull of Galloway would reach northern Ireland after a sea crossing of only 40 km, and the SW track also involves a relatively short distance of 150 km, to Dublin Bay. However, birds on a track between SSW and S would run a risk of missing both Ireland and Wales unless they showed a dawn reorientation such as Myres (1964) described for the northern North Sea. Such birds could find themselves west of the Scillies at first light. Broadfront movements at night to the SSW over the northern Irish Sea were seen on radar in the late autumn of 1959 by Bourne (1978). Bourne also deduced that with strong northerly winds the birds might find themselves at dawn over the Atlantic to the south west of Ireland but thought that many could have overflown southern Ireland rather than missing land altogether. Bourne saw in addition a movement to the SSE that does not appear in my moonwatch results; this is probably a local effect due simply to the fact that there is practically no land to the NNW of the Mull of Galloway that could act as a source of migrants.

INCIDENCE OF CALLS DURING PASSAGE

Many birds called at night over the Mull of Galloway even on clear moonlit nights whereas, as in previous years, this does not occur at Alva. The most likely explanation is that at Alva they have just crossed 600m hills and are too high to be heard. Alternatively, the presence of the sea may stimulate calling whereas when overland in clear conditions they are silent. I have been unable to find published evidence about whether night migrants can be heard on clear moonlit nights over inland and low lying areas.

70 NUMBERS OF BIRDS SEEN AT NIGHT AND THE NEXT DAY

At the Mull of Galloway there is in general a very poor correlation between migrants crossing the moon and those grounded next morning. It is not surprising if few migrants land on the Mull with a clear dawn since birds can see land across the North Channel or detect Luce Bay and land before reaching it. It is, however, surprising that maximum numbers of all migrant passerines were seen on the morning of October 14, after negligible moonwatch passage the evening before. The misty conditions at dawn would have greatly increased the chance of night migrants landing on the Mull but I find it difficult to believe that the slight passage indicated by the early moonwatch could have been sufficient. One possibility is that a moderate passage did not reach Galloway until later in the night. However, Bourne (pers. comm.) did not see any southwesterly departure from northeast Scotland on radar and the large number of Redwing calls heard over Galloway in the evening has still to be explained. I had the impression from the calls and the directions of the few birds seen (Table 1) that they were flying in a confused manner at a low height — this last possibility would also explain why only one was seen crossing the moon. Moreover it had been very cloudy since sunset and again after the end of the moonwatch, so that conditions were not good for normal migration, even though it is certain that many Scandinavian migrants had arrived in Scotland and were available to form an onward passage in the light easterly wind. The simplest explanation is that many birds started a nocturnal flight but in a poorly oriented manner at low altitude. It is possible that little net progress was made but in any case conditions would be right for a fall of dawn migrants on an isolated peninsula like the Mull. By comparison, Wilcock (1965) noted similar inconsistency between radar data and counts from the Isle of May and ascribed some discrepancies to birds failing to alight at the observatory and others to birds migrating too low to be detected by radar.

CONCLUSIONS

The results presented here show a SSW direction of migration over the northern Irish sea which is quite consistent with observations by radar. There is support for a previous conclusion that night migrants over central Scotland in mid-autumn primarily originate from Scandinavia and many continue across to Ireland although a substantial proportion at the Mull of Galloway are on tracks that would, if maintained, take them across the full length of the Irish sea or even out into the western approaches. Further work needs to be **71** done on the incidence of calling during migration flights.

ACKNOWLEDGEMENT

I am very grateful to Mrs. J. Lammie for arranging accommodation for my family at the Mull of Galloway and to W. R. Brackenridge for drawing the illustration.

REFERENCES

BOURNE, W. R. P. 1978. Observations with radar of bird migration across the northern Irish Sea in the late autumn of 1959. *Irish Birds* 1, 199-206.
HENTY, C. J. 1978. A moonwatch study of nocturnal migration over central Scotland. *Scottish Birds* 10, 2-10.
LACK, D. 1969. Drift migration: a correction. *Ibis* 111, 253-255.
MYRES, M. T. 1964. Dawn ascent and reorientation of Scandinavian thrushes (*Turdus* spp.) migrating at night over the north-eastern Atlantic ocean in the autumn. *Ibis* 106, 7-51.
WILCOCK, J. 1965. Detection by radar of autumn migration in eastern Scotland. *Ibis* 316-325.

Place	Date	Wind	Obs. Span. (GMT)	Directions					Total	Time (mins)	Calls
				WSW	SW	SSW	S	Other			
Alva	12	Mod.WSW	18.25—20.22	19	8	2		3W, 1WNW	33	83	0
"	18	Calm	20.34—21.04		1	2			3	30	0
Totals, Central Scotland				19	9	4	0	4	36		0
Mull of Galloway	13	Lt E	21.45—22.35					1WNW	1	50	25*
" " "	15	NW/5	19.50—20.48	3	5	6	2	1W, 1WNW	18	51	55
" " "	17	Lt N	20.38—21.51	2	9	11	10	1NE	33	69	70
Totals, Mull of Galloway				5	14	17	12	4	52		150

These calls came from birds that seemed to be milling about; also three birds were seen close to the moon heading, N, S and E.

Table I Moonface directions and calls of night migrants in Central Scotland (Alva) and Mull of Galloway, October, 1978.

72

THE TRUE BUGS (HETEROPTERA)
OF TENTSMUIR POINT, FIFE

James K. Campbell

INTRODUCTION

Coastal sand dunes have long been recognised as important sites for plants and animals which often exhibit peculiarities confined to this type of formation. Insects have received much attention, although little ecological work has been attempted. Important papers include those by van Heerdt and Morzer Bruyns (1960) and Cotton (1967) who studied the insect fauna in relation to the stages of succession, comparing the mobile dunes with the more fixed dunes inland. More comprehensive ecological analyses have been done on the spider fauna of sand dunes by Duffy (1968) and Almquist (1973) who studied the habitat preferences of spiders over the whole range

of habitats found on dune systems. One of Duffy's study areas was **73**
Tentsmuir Point.

This paper gives the results of a study of the habitat preferences
of one particular group of insects, the true bugs (Heteroptera), at
Tentsmuir Point NNR (National Nature Reserve) during the summer
of 1978. These insects feed on the sap of plants, and are closely
related to Homopteran bugs (aphids and frog-hoppers). A few species
have developed a predatory habit. Both groups belong to the order
Hemiptera.

Tentsmuir Point is situated in the north-east corner of Fife,
bounded on the north side by the Firth of Tay, and on the west by a
mature pine plantation. The Reserve comprises a coastal strip two km
long and up to 0.75 km wide, providing a fine example of a relatively
undisturbed, actively growing, dune system. The climate of Tentsmuir
is mild and the area is one of the sunniest in Scotland, although
suffering periods of heavy rain. The average annual rainfall is 75 cms
(30 inches). The Tentsmuir sand has a low lime content and as a
result an acid flora has developed on the stable dunes inland. Previous
collections of insects at Tentsmuir have shown the Reserve to have
considerable entomological interest. Of particular relevance is a
collection of true bugs, which is discussed later, made by Malcolm
Smith (unpublished) between 1963 and 1967.

CLASSIFICATION OF THE ANIMAL HABITATS

The landward part of Tentsmuir Point NNR comprises
approximately 52 ha (130 acres) yet within this small area there is a
remarkable diversity of plants which provide a wide range of habitats
for bugs. Several attempts at classifying the vegetation have been
made, e.g. Fairley (1977) and Duffy (1968), however none of these
classifications were found to be suitable for bugs, which are often
confined to one food plant with a very patchy distribution.

For the purposes of this study the Reserve was split up into 13
broad habitat types, briefly described below, and shown in Figures 1
and 2. The dominant plants found in each habitat are given in Table
1, in which English names are from Dony, Perring and Rob (1974).

A Drift Line.   This is composed of an accumulation of flotsam,
jetsam and dead organic material deposited by spring high tides.
No growing vegetation is present.
B Embryo Dune.   These dunes form an extensive area at the north
of the reserve and consist of unstable low-lying dunes colonised
sparsely by grasses.

74 C Marram Grass Dune. The highest and most prominent of the semi-stable dunes are colonised by marram grass with few other plants present.

D Lyme-Grass Dune. The semi-stable dunes are lower in the north-east and here lyme-grass takes over from marram grass. In July a number of herbaceous plants grow up amongst the lyme-grass.

E Marram Transition. On the landward side of the semi-stable dunes the marram grass begins to lose vigour and is less often found growing in tussocks. There is more bare ground but many other plants may be found amongst the marram grass. This is a more open habitat than the two preceding ones.

F Dune Slack (1): Grass/Sedge Type. The larger and more northern part of the main slack is dominated by grasses and sedges, together with some rushes.

G Dune Slack (2): Creeping Willow/Birdsfoot Trefoil Type. The southern half of the main slack is dominated by creeping willow and birdsfoot trefoil.

All the dune slacks on the Reserve are often flooded with fresh water during the winter and spring, and in summer support a rich profusion of flowering plants.

H Dune Heath (1): Lichen/Moss Type. Dune Heath covers a large area of the Reserve on the inland side of the slacks. Scots pines have been allowed to grow over a large part of this habitat, splitting it into two. Now areas of true Dune Heath are found in the north and south of the reserve, with a large section of young pine woodland in the centre.

I Dune Heath (2): Heather Type. This is a small area in the most northerly part of the Reserve where heather is dominant.

J Alder Line. The Alder Line was formed by alder colonising a dune slack and it now consists of a narrow strip of woodland running parallel to the shoreline across most of the Reserve.

K Birch/Willow Scrub. Small areas of silver birch and willow are present in several moist localities.

L Pine/Birch Woodland. This covers a large area in the centre of the Reserve where Scots pine has colonised the Dune Heath to the exclusion of many plants common in the latter habitat.

M Marshy Slack. The Marshy Slack is situated in the southern half of the Reserve along the western boundary and has typical marsh plants.

N Aquatic. The only permanently aquatic habitat on the Reserve is a 200 m Forestry Commission drainage ditch which flows slowly along the southern edge of the Reserve.

Table 1   Dominant Plants found in each habitat   **75**

A Drift Line	C Marram Dune	D Lyme-Grass Dune
No growing vegetation	Marram Grass	Lyme-grass
		Spear Thistle
B Embryo Dune		Rosebay Willowherb
		Common Ragwort
Sand Couch Grass		
Lyme-Grass		

E Marram Transition	F Dune Slack (1)	G Dune Slack (2)
Marram Grass	Creeping Bent Grass	Creeping Willow
Mosses	Sedges	Birdsfoot Trefoil
Rosebay Willowherb	Grass-of-Parnassus	Silver Birch
Spear Thistle	Northern Marsh Orchid	
Ragwort	Silver Birch	
	Seaside Centaury	
	Yellow Rattle	

H Dune Heath (1)	I Dune Heath (2)	J Alder Line
Lichens	Heather	Alder
Mosses	Sweet Briar	Silver Birch
Lady's Bedstraw	Broom	Yorkshire-fog
Sweet Briar	Gorse	Skullcap
Broom		
Gorse		

K Birch/Willow Scrub	L Pine/Birch Woodland	M Marshy Slack
Silver Birch	Scots pine	Common Sedge
Grey Willow		Reed Sweet Grass
Cross-leaved Heath	N Aquatic	Soft Rush
Heather		Meadowsweet
Mosses	Common Water-crowfoot	Skullcap
	Marsh-marigold	Silverweed

METHODS

Systematic collecting began on 7 July 1978 and continued for six weeks. Standard entomological collecting methods were used including sweeping and beating vegetation and searching on the ground in litter and moss. Several hours were spent collecting in each habitat and every major plant was sampled. Most habitats were sampled twice during the study period. Generally collecting was not attempted on days when the vegetation was very wet or temperatures were low.

Specimens were identified using Southwood and Leston (1959) and Macan (1965). Representative specimens were checked against reference material in the Royal Scottish Museum or Dundee Museum. A small number of specimens were identified by Alan Stubbs (Nature Conservancy Council) and Rodger Waterston (Royal Scottish Museum). Nomenclature of bugs follow Kloet and Hincks (1964).

RESULTS

Sixty-two species were collected in the present study bringing the total number of species recorded for the reserve to 90, a large number for such a small area in northern Britain. Table 2 gives the number of species collected from each habitat type. The complete list of species collected is given in Table 3, together with an indication of their abundance. Aquatic bugs are given separately in Table 4.

Table 2   Total number of species in each habitat

	Drift Line	Embryo Dune	Marram Dune	Lyme-grass Dune	Marram Transition	Dune Slack (1)	Dune Slack (2)	Dune Heath (1)	Dune Heath (2)	Alder Line	Birch/Willow Scrub	Pine/Birch Woodland	Marshy Slack	Aquatic
HABITAT	A	B	C	D	E	F	G	H	I	J	K	L	M	N
Number of Species	0	4	5	11	4	13	10	22	11	18	12	20	17	6

DISCUSSION

As expected, the number of Heteropteran bugs increases as one passes inland from the Embryo Dunes to the Dune Heath (Table 2). This may be due to the corresponding increase in plant diversity, but other contributing factors may include the physical instability and exposure of the seaward habitats.

Several bugs were ubiquitous, taken from a variety of plants throughout the reserve. For example, *Anthocoris nemoralis, A. nemorum, Plagiognathus chrysanthemi, Plesiocoris rugicollis, Calocoris norvegicus,* and *Leptoterna ferrugata* were abundant in seven or more habitats. Similarly, the shore bug *Saldula saltatoria* was found in seven habitats, although the absence of other saldids is puzzling. Some bugs are restricted to uncommon food plants, e.g. *Dicythus annulatus* was taken from restharrow, and *Orthops rubricatus* from a single sitka spruce tree.

On habitats A—E, which cover the mobile and semi-fixed dunes of the Reserve, few bugs were collected, probably due to low plant diversity. The Embryo Dunes, perhaps the most exposed terrestrial habitat on the reserve, supported little insect life including very few bugs. Of the bugs collected, *Trigonotylus psammaecolor* was the most noteworthy, all individuals being taken on the landward side of the Embryo Dunes. This is a bug which is only found on coastal sand dunes and so it may be classed as a 'psammophile' (van Heerdt·and Morzer Bruyns 1960). It was taken from sand couch and marram grass during July. The Marram Dunes, on the other hand, have been shown to contain a wide variety of invertebrate life (Cotton 1967, Duffy 1968), and this is reflected in the larger number of bugs found here, and the presence of the predatory bugs *Anthocoris nemoralis* and *Saldula saltatoria.* Two other species, *Trigonotylus ruficornis* and *Leptoterna ferrugata* regularly feed on marram grass and were taken from this plant wherever it occurred on the Reserve. The Marram Transition habitat, although containing a few more plants, supported a similar fauna to that of the Marram Dunes. The Lyme-grass Dunes supported a much larger bug fauna than the previous two because of the large numbers of thistles and ragwort which grew up there in July.

The Dune Slacks contained two of the most interesting and important bugs on the Reserve. These are *Coranus subapterus* and *Systellonotus triguttatus,* and for both Tentsmuir Point is one of very few Scottish locations. *C. subapterus,* the Heath Assassin bug, is a large predatory bug feeding on a variety of small invertebrates. It was found on bare ground near creeping willow; both macropterus (long wing) and brachypterous (short wing) forms were taken, the former being rare in Southern England. *S. triguttatus* is normally found

78 TABLE 3   Estimates of abundance of each species in each habitat except 'Drift Line' (all zero) and 'Aquatic'.

A = Abundant   C = Common   R = Rare   L = Local, i.e. taken from a locally distributed plant within the habitat

SPECIES	Embryo Dune	Marram Dune	Lyme-grass Dune	Marram Transition	Dune Slack (1)	Dune Slack (2)	Dune Heath (1)	Dune Heath (2)	Alder Line	Birch/Willow Scrub	Pine/Birch Woodland	Marshy Slack
	B	C	D	E	F	G	H	I	J	K	L	M
Elasmostethus interstinctus									C	C		
Elasmucha grisea										R		
Pentatoma rufipes						C			A	A		A
Nysius thymi				C	C				C			
Stygnocoris pedestris												C
Drymus brunneus										C		
Scolopostethus decoratus												R
S. thomsoni									RL			
Coranus subapterus						C						
Anthocoris nemoralis	C						A	C	C	C	C	A
*A. nemorum						A	A	A	A	A	A	A
A. sarothamni							RL					
Acompocoris pygmaeus											C	
Nabis ferus			R									
Monalocoris filicis							CL				R	
*Psallus ambiguus										R		
Psallus betuleti					C	A				A		R
P. roseus											C	
*Phoenicocoris obscurellus											C	
Attractotomus magnicornis											CL	
*Plagiognathus arbustorum			A				A		R		A	A
P. chrysanthemi			A		A	A	A	A	A			A
Asciodema obsoletum							CL	CL				
Systellonotus triguttatus					C	C						
Dicyphus annulatus							CL					
Pachytomella parallela					A							
Heterocordylus genistae					A							

TABLE 3   (Continued)

A = Abundant   C = Common   P = Rare   L = Local, i.e. taken
from a locally
distributed plant
within the habitat

SPECIES	B	C	D	E	F	G	H	I	J	K	L	M
H. tibialis					C			CL				
Blepharidopterus angulatus							C					
Orthotylus adenocarpi								RL				
O. ericetorum						C	C					
O. virescens							CL	CL				
Mecomma albulans								C	C	C	C	
Pithanus maerkeli				C		C	C			C	C	
Lygus maritimus			C			C						
L. rugulipennis							C			C		
L. wagneri												
Orthops cervinus								RL				
O. rubricatus										CL		
Lygocoris pabulinus		C	C			A		A		A	A	
L. contaminatus				A	A			A	A	A		
L. viridis		C						C				
Camptozygum pinastri										A		
Plesiocoris rugicollis		C			A	C		A	A	A	A	
Dichrooscytus rufipennis										C		
Miris striatus								R				
Calocoris norvegicus	R	A	A	A		A	A			A	A	
Adelphocoris lineolatus												
Phytocoris pini										C		
P. tiliae								R				
Stenodema holsatum											R	
Trigonotylus psammaecolor	C	C										
T. ruficornis		A		A	A	A	A					
Leptoterna dolobrata		C					C				C	
L. ferrugata	A	A	A	A	A	A	A	C			A	
Saldula saltatoria		C			A	A	A	A		A	A	

*The identification of those species marked with an asterisk has been checked by
A. Stubbs (Nature Conservancy Council) or A. R. Waterston (Royal Scottish
Museum).

80 south of a line from Lincoln to Carmarthen. It is usually found in
open sandy heaths in association with ants, and at Tentsmuir Point it
was found in the Dune Slacks where ants are common. The female is
an ant mimic. Apart from these two species, the bug fauna of the
slacks consist of common species normally associated with damp
grassy situations in Scotland.

The Dune Heath has the most diverse vegetation in the Reserve
and this was reflected by the large number of bug species found
there. Among the more interesting were *Dicythus annulatus,
Adelphocoris lineolatus,* both found on restharrow, and *Lygus
wagneri* on tansy. Few bugs were taken from nettles, and the single
trees of juniper and rowan had no bugs. Lichens and mosses
dominate the ground vegetation and no bugs were collected there.

The Heather area at the north end of the reserve was much poorer
in bugs and surprisingly only one heather-feeding species was
collected, *Orthotylus ericetorum.* The few broom brushes, however,
revealed an interesting fauna including *Anthocoris sarothamni,
Orthotylus adenocarpi* and *O. virescens.* Very few bugs were found
on the numerous rose bushes.

The Pine/Birch Woodland was also rich in bugs, although several of
these were confined to Scots Pine, e.g. *Phytocoris pini, Phoenicocoris
obscurellus, Camptozygum pinastri* and *Dichrooscytus rufipennis.*
Scots pine appears to be a rich food plant for bugs on the reserve.
One sitka spruce tree was sampled in mid-August and this revealed
two additional species, *Attractotomus magnicornis* and *Orthops
rubricatus.* The latter species is confined to spruces.

It is interesting to compare the Dune Heath fauna with that of the
Pine/Birch Woodland, for the latter habitat may be considered as a
development of the former, although an unnatural one following the
regeneration of Scots pine from the mature plantation bordering the
Reserve. From Table 3 it is apparent that ten species are common to
both habitats and it is noticeable that all are common bugs found in
most parts of the Reserve. In the case of the Pine/Birch Woodland,
these bugs were all taken from common plants (e.g. grasses, ragwort)
in small clearings in the wood. Of the remaining ten species collected
from this habitat, all are associated with conifers, with the exception
of *Psallus roseus* which was found on creeping willow near the edge
of the wood. Hence the majority of bugs associated with the Dune
Heath are absent from the Pine/Birch Woodland. This study suggests
therefore that the result of the encroachment of the Scots pines has
been the gradual extinction of those bugs feeding on heather, gorse,
broom and restharrow and the invasion and spread of pine-feeding
species over the last ten years or so. Reserve management policy aims
at excluding Scots pines from all Dune Heath areas, and this was

extended in late 1978 to include the Marshy Slack and Pine/Birch **81**
Woodland. It is expected that all conifer species will be gradually
removed from these areas in the future.

The Alder Line also supported a large number of species, all
typical of deciduous trees. The northern half of the Alder Line was
found to support more species than the southern half probably due
to the lush vegetation growing beneath the trees: the predatory bug
Miris striatus, was found there. As expected, the Birch/Willow Scrub
had a similar fauna to that of the Alder Line. *Elasmucha grisea,* a
shield bug, was taken from birch, and the damp ground vegetation
revealed *Drymus brunneus,* a ground bug feeding on mosses.

The Marshy Slack, although small in area, supported a large
number of bugs. All of the 17 species, however, are common and
normally associated with wet marshy habitats. Meadowsweet, when it
grew up in August, was found to be very rich in bugs; five species
were collected from it on one occasion.

The Aquatic habitat was sampled on two occasions: for such a
short stretch of water, a large number of species was collected. All
are typical of slow-moving lowland streams.

COMPARISON WITH OTHER COLLECTIONS

Various entomological collections have been made at Tentsmuir
Point, the most important being a collection of Coleoptera and
Heteroptera made by Malcolm Smith in 1963-67 while employed as
Reserve Warden. Details of the Heteropteran bugs collected by M.
Smith are given in Table 5 (pers. comm.). In addition, E. C.
Pelham-Clinton collected the following species on visits in 1970;
Rhacognathus punctatus, swept from creeping willow, and
Chartoscirta cincta, smoked from lyme-grass (pers. comm.). Also R.
A. Crowson collected *Ceratocombus coleoptratus* in 1972 (Crowson
1972).

An examination of the above lists reveals that my collections
added fourteen new species to the Reserve but I did not find
twenty-six species previously recorded. These discrepancies require
some comment.

Many of those in the first category feed on trees and M. Smith has
suggested that he missed them because he only sampled with a sweep
net (pers. comm.). Furthermore, I sampled the aquatic habitat more
extensively and this alone accounts for four new species.

The absence of the twenty-six species in the second category may
be attributed to a number of factors. First of all, it should be noted
that M. Smith made his collections over a period of five years,

TABLE 4   Water Bugs collected from Aquatic Habitat

Gerris thoracicus   Corixa punctata
Notonecta Glauca   Callicorixa praeusta
Sigara dorsalis   *Hesperocorixa salbergi

*Checked by A. Stubbs or A. R. Waterston

TABLE 5   Heteropteran Bugs collected by M. Smith, at Tentsmuir Point
           NNR, 1963-67

Pentatoma rufipes	Monalocoris filicis	Lygocoris contaminatus
Piezodorus lituratus	Bothynotis pilosus	L. pabulinus
Picromerus bidens	Conostethus brevis	L. viridis
Nysius thymi	Psallus ambiguus	Plesiocoris rugicollis
Kleidocerys truncatulus	P. betuleti	Camptozygum pinastri
Stygnocoris pedestris	P. roseus	Polymerus unifasciatus
S. rusticus	Atractotomus magnicornis	Dichrooscytus rufipennis
Drymus brunneus	Plagiognathus arbustonum	Callocoris norvegicus
Scolopostethus affinis	P. chrysanthemi	C. roseomaculatus
S. decoratus	Asciodema absoletum	Adelphocoris lineolatus
S. thomsoni	Hallodapus rufescens	Capsus ater
Gastrodes grossipes	Systellonotus triguttatus	Stenodema calcaratum
Piesma quadratum	Dicyphus annulatus	S. holsatum
Acalypta nigrina	Packytomella parallela	Trigonotylus psammaecolor
A. parvula	Heterocordylus tibialis	T. ruficornis
Derephysia foliacea	Blepharidopterus	Leptopterna dolobrata
Tingis cardui	angulatus	L. ferrugata
Nabis ferus	Orthotylus ericetorum	Ceratocombus coleoptratus
N. flavomarginatus	Mecomma albulans	Saldula orthochila
Dolichonobis limbatus	Pithanus maerkeli	S. saltatoria
Anthocoris confusus	Lygus maritimus	Velia caprai
A. nemoralis	L. rugulipennis	Gerris lateralis
A. nemorum	L. wagneri	Notonecta glauca
A. sarothamni	Orthops cervinus	Corixa punctata
Acompocoris pygmaeus	Liocoris tripustulatus	Sigara nigrolineata

whereas I collected for only six weeks of one summer. Some species **83** may have been missed because they emerged earlier or later than the study period. This may account for *Stygnocoris rusticus, Nabis ferus, Stenodema calcaratum, Liocoris tripustulatus,* and *Ceratocombus coleoptratus* not being found in the present survey.

Another important factor may be the effect of habitat changes since M. Smith made his collection. Firstly, it is several years since the Dune Slacks were regularly flooded with seawater at spring high tides. This may account for the absence of *Piesma quodratum* and *Conostethus brevis* which feed on Halophytes, presumably more common on the Reserve at that time. Secondly, M. Smith collected three species of ground bugs (Lygaeidae) from nettles, *Scolopostethus affinis, S. thomsoni, Liocoris tripustulatus.* Of these only one was taken by the present author and it was rare. Nettles appear to have decreased on the Reserve recently and this may account for the apparent absence of the other two species. Thirdly, a succession of wet winters and springs has resulted in prolonged flooding in the area of the Marshy Slack during the last few years. Many bugs are susceptible to attack by fungi when overwintering, and this may affect their survival under wet conditions. In 1978, the luxuriant plant growth normally associated with this habitat did not grow up until September, after collecting had ceased. There is also a possibility that my collecting in this habitat may not have been intensive enough. Any or all these factors may account for the absence of species such as *Acalypta nigrina, A. parvula, Derephysia foliacea, Bothynotus pilosus,* and *Ceratocombus coleoptratus.*

ACKNOWLEDGEMENTS

I would like to thank A. Stubbs and A. R. Waterston for identifying specimens, R. Brinklow (Dundee Museum) and E. C. Pelham-Clinton (Royal Scottish Museum) for allowing me to consult their collections, and M. Nelson, R. Keymer and M. Smith for helpful criticisms of the manuscript.

REFERENCES

ALMQUIST, B. 1973. Spider associations in coastal sand dunes. *Oikos* 24, 444-457.
COTTON, M. J. 1967. Aspects of the ecology of sand dune arthropods. *Entomologist* 100, 157-165.
CROWSON, R. A. 1972. A macropterous *Ceratocombus coleoptratus* (Zett.) (Hem., Dipsocoridae) in Scotland. *Entomologists' Monthly Magazine* 108, 247.

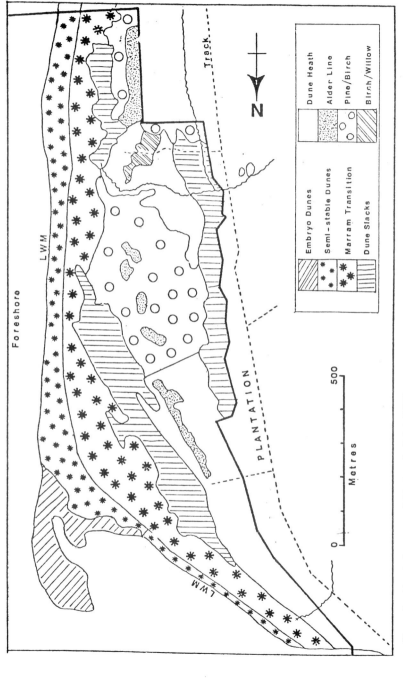

Figure 1   Vegetation map of Tentsmuir Point NNR

DONY, J. D. PERRING, F. H. and ROB, C. M. 1974. English Names of Wild Flowers. Butterworth, London.

DUFFY, E. 1968. An ecological analysis of the spider fauna of sand dunes. *Journal of Animal Ecology* 37, 641-674.

FAIRLEY, R. 1977. Summer Wardens Report, Tentsmuir Point NNR. Nature Conservancy Council, Internal Report.

HEERDT, P. F. VAN and BRUYNS, M. F. MORZER, 1960. A biocenological investigation in the Yellow Dune Region of Terscheling, Sweden. *Tijdschrift voor Entomologie* 103, 225-275.

HINCKS, W. D. 1951. The entomology of the Spurn Peninsula. *Naturalist* 1951, 139-146.

KLOET, G. S. and HINCKS, W. D. 1964. A Check List of British Insects, 2nd edition, part 1 Small orders and Hemiptera. *Handbooks for the Identification of British Insects* II(I), 36-52.

MACAN, T. T. 1965. A Key to British Water Bugs. Freshwater Biological Association.

SOUTHWOOD, T. R. E. and LESTON, D. 1959. Land and Water Bugs of the British Isles. F. Warne, London and New York.

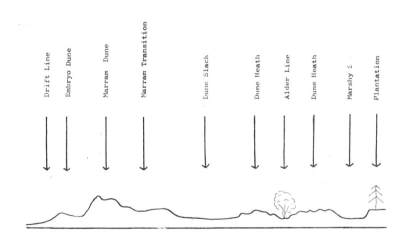

Figure 2   Diagrammatic representation of habitats at Tentsmuir Point along a hypothetical cross-section

Allan Water

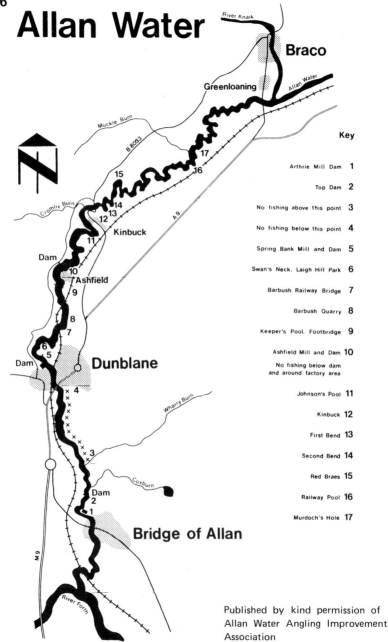

Braco

Greenloaning

Key

Arthrie Mill Dam **1**

Top Dam **2**

No fishing above this point **3**

No fishing below this point **4**

Spring Bank Mill and Dam **5**

Swan's Neck. Laigh Hill Park **6**

Barbush Railway Bridge **7**

Barbush Quarry **8**

Keeper's Pool. Footbridge **9**

Ashfield Mill and Dam **10**
No fishing below dam
and around factory area

Johnson's Pool **11**

Kinbuck **12**

First Bend **13**

Second Bend **14**

Red Braes **15**

Railway Pool **16**

Murdoch's Hole **17**

Kinbuck

Dam

Ashfield

Dunblane

Dam

Bridge of Allan

Published by kind permission of
Allan Water Angling Improvement
Association

ASHFIELD 87
A FACTORY VILLAGE IN SOUTH PERTHSHIRE

John D. Williams

The nineteenth century saw Britain transformed from an agricultural to an industrial nation, and the majority of its inhabitants become town dwellers. Yet most industrial developments in the late eighteenth and early nineteenth century were in rural surroundings, particularly on the fringes of upland areas where fast running streams provided power for mills not only before the advent of steam, but in some cases well into the present century. Particularly in the textile industries where large quantities of water were required for washing processes as well as power, the availability of steampower was an additional factor in the production processes rather than an alternative to a riverside site.

The mill village thus became a common form of settlement during the nineteenth century, often becoming absorbed into nearby towns as these grew, or becoming the nucleus of larger settlements where mills were in close proximity to one another. Except in the west, however, the population densities of Scotland and the restricted size of most mill sites have left many of these villages relatively untouched by subsequent development. Because the power available from a river is dependent on the head of water between the dam and the river below the mill, there is a natural limit to the expansion likely on a given site, and therefore such waterpowered mills are less likely to be expanded and rebuilt just because they are successful, thus destroying the original layout.

Interest in these factory villages has naturally focused on the earliest examples, and on the most influential. Robert Owen's New Lanark, and the Buchanan brothers' Deanston are well known, but little research has been done on the scores of less notable examples that not only transformed the British economy and created a new form of community, but in many cases were successful enough to continue unchanged for over a century. A number of such villages exist in the Forth valley, attracting attention to themselves only when the mill closes, as did Ashfield by Dunblane in 1976, after 110 years of operation. Unless local historians investigate such important surviving relics of the industrial revolution now, whilst not only the buildings, but the people who lived and worked in them are still able to tell us of their function, an invaluable source for the social and technological history of Scotland will be lost.

This paper on Ashfield is presented therefore, not because this particular factory village was of great importance except to those

88 who lived there, but because it may well have been more typical than more famous contemporary developments, and because too often in history we are told only of the exceptional, as no one bothers to record the ordinary. Yet with the growing interest of many people in the history of their immediate locality, this paper, based on just one visit to a local solicitor and one interview with a family resident in the village, and one evening reading all references to Ashfield in the *Stirling Journal and Advertiser* using the University of Stirling's invaluable *Local Index* to that newspaper (Volume 2, 1979) is the type of project that can be carried out by any amateur historian, yet which could be of great benefit as source material for historians in the future.

It was in 1865 that the lands of Mill Ash or Wester Ashfold, situated in a loop of the Allan Water three kilometres north of Dunblane, and adjacent to the Scottish Central Railway, was sold by John Stirling of Kippendavie to Messrs. J. & J. Pullar & Company, Manufacturers Bleachers and Dyers, of Keirfield, Bridge of Allan. (John Pullar and his son were related to their famous namesakes at Perth, but the Bridge of Allan company was a separate commercial entity). The feu disposition specifically included land and ' the water power of the River Allan connected with the piece of land.' For reasons that are not completely clear, although most of the site was sold outright to Pullars, the northern tip was only leased. It was a condition of the sale that ' within the space of eighteen months...to erect and build upon the ground hereby disponed Dwellinghouses or Manufactures, Factories or workshops or other buildings of the value of not less than One thousand two hundred and fifty pounds Sterling with all necessary Engines and Machinery, and that upon any of the sites shown upon the said Plan...which plan has now been approved by me. ...Provided always that no building except the Buildings shewn upon the said Plan...shall be erected...and that the ground unbuilt upon shall be used exclusively for garden or planting, or as pleasure grounds, or for ordinary agricultural purposes, or for bleaching and dyeing...except in such cases as the deviation may be specifically authorised by the Superior for the time being.'

A brief comparison of this plan (Figure 1), with the plan (Figure 2) attached to a disposition of 1909 when the land only leased in 1865 was finally purchased by Pullars, shows that the village actually built was considerably more ambitious than the plan agreed between the parties in 1865. The factory was built exactly as shown in the original feu disposition, although it was subsequently extended. That the factory shape and size were correctly anticipated, but that five straight rows of cottages distributed at odd angles all over the site should by the next year become a formal 'square' at the furthest end of the site from the factory, would suggest that although Pullar had planned the factory, he had not really thought about the housing requirements in 1865, but was able to produce a 'model village' in 1866. Obviously an architect was commissioned for this work, but the point is that Pullar was willing to engage a good professional architect to build an attractive village for what was after all only a small branch factory.

By concentrating the village at the narrow end of the site they were able to both create a spacious setting for the manager's house, and to give over the larger part of the ground to stables, cowsheds and agricultural buildings. The purpose of these was not only to provide dairy produce for the village, but more particularly to provide the horses for transport of cloth to and from Bridge of Allan. Although the plan of 1909 shows the village to have its own railway siding, only coal and chemicals arrived by rail. All cloth for processing came by horsedrawn cart from Keirfield, seven kilometres away, and the finished cloth returned by the same method of transport for cutting and dispatch. This system of using horses continued until the mid nineteen-thirties, when Pullars purchased their first petrol lorry.

The factory was built for the printing (especially roller printing) and beetling of cotton cloth. Messrs. Pullar of Bridge of Allan were famous for their waistcoat linings, and the new rotary machine for printing stripes installed at Ashfield was obviously of great advantage. The beetling process, whereby a high finish was obtained by the cloth having heavy beech blocks hammered up and down on it for forty-eight hours, was obviously extravagant in space and power. Although necessary for the most expensive of their linings, it was an obvious candidate for removal to Ashfield where power was plentiful — the river provided approximately 800-900 horsepower by its natural fall whilst sweeping round the factory; it was not even necessary to build a lade. Water turbines were still the main power source for the factory until its closure in 1976, but heat and steam were required in the dyeing and drying of the cloth, so the tall chimney which was the first sight one had of Ashfield as the road approached from Dunblane was also an original feature, making sense of the mill's location between the river and the railway. This chimney was demolished in 1979. Coal and dyestuffs were delivered to Ashfield siding, but the subordinate nature of the factory to Keirfield, the main Bridge of Allan factory, and its relatively low output, made horsedrawn transport more economic for the cloth. Steam also provided auxiliary power in summer when the river was low.

90 The Allan Water is relatively slow moving above Ashfield, and a shallow weir to the north of the village with only a short lade drove a waterpump that raised good drinkingwater from a spring in the railway embankment to the reservoir beside the factory. The large weir at the mill would obviously be the site of the old Mill of Ashie mentioned in the title deed of 1865, and would presumably have been at least rapids, if not a waterfall, prior to that. Pullars' Keirfield Mill at Bridge of Allan was the furthest downstream of all the mills along the Allan before it joined the Forth. Many more mills, for corn, paper, wool and timber sawing were distributed between a point just to the north of Dunblane, where the Allan moves into a deep gorge and drops rapidly, and the Keirfield Mill. Ashfield was therefore not only located on a powerful river convenient to the railway only seven kilometres distant from the main factory, it was also upstream of most of the other industrial users, whereas Kierfield was downstream of them all. Since it was the most expensive linings that were to be produced at the new factory, the purity of the water supply would be an important factor, and a bleacher and dyer owning the furthest downstream of some twenty mills in seven kilometres would have known exactly his requirements in this respect. Site location would therefore seem to have been carried out with considerable care in this instance.

The one remaining question, of why this perfect site had not been developed previously, is answered in the 1865 feu disposition. All the estates owned by John Stirling of Kippendavie were entailed, and it was only the Acts of Parliament allowing the sale of such land in certain circumstances of 1852, and Stirling's subsequent petition to the Lords of Council of 1858, that cleared the legal barriers to the sale of this land. It could therefore not have been developed except by Stirling himself prior to 1858, so when due time is allowed for negotiations, 1865 is not an unreasonable date for the first industrial use of a comparatively remote site, despite its considerable advanatages in all but one respect.

Ashfield offered space, power, communications and easf transport, and plentiful clean water for bleaching, dyeing and hu an consumption. One factor only was missing — labour. The nearest village, Kinbuck, is a small agricultural community with a woollen mill and school, but would not have had the surplus labour nor housing to provide for an additional workforce of about two hundred people. The need to provide housing was therefore implicit once the site was chosen, although this was a new situation for Pullars, as their Bridge of Allan factory was on the edge of a thriving Spa town that lacked only sufficient industrial employment. They did own a terrace of four small cottages at Bridge of Allan, but it is of interest that only after the building of Ashfield village did they build more houses for their workers at Bridge of Allan, eventually owning fourteen cottages by 1880.

The plan of 1865 would suggest that the Pullars were not far advanced in their planning of Ashfield village at that time, yet its completion in 1866 was to an attractive layout with single storey dwellings in blocks of three along both long sides of The Square and across the north end, and small blocks of privies, coalsheds and wash-houses between each terrace. The south side of the square was a two storied block, with the ground floor houses entered from the square, and the upper houses entered by external stairs to the rear. The eastern half of this block as shown on the 1909 plan is not part of the original design, but is an extension of 1898 disturbing the original symmetry of the Square.

The most southerly of the single storey terraces on the Square was actually built earlier than the rest of the village and was of a different construction. This block had been built by the Scottish Central Railway Company for their workers when constructing the railway cutting beside the village. Tradition in the village is that there was originally a tunnel which was converted to a cutting when it partially collapsed. This block, demolished in 1976, was inferior to the rest, being built on the common close principle from poured concrete, unlike the sandstone of the rest of the village. One of my informants was brought up as a member of a family of six girls and one boy living in one room and a kitchen in 'the Concrete', so knew the building well, yet did not regret its demolition.

The Manager's house (Ash Cottage) was comprised of six rooms, kitchen and bathroom, and stood beside the factory at the southern end of the site. This and the farm and steadings, all of 1866, were well spread out over the central section of the site. On 13th May, 1898, however, the *Stirling Journal* reported that ' in order to provide additional accommodation for their increasing staff of workers ... (Messrs. Pullar) ... are presently erecting light new dwellinghouses there' . These new blocks were mainly two storied terraces, and increased the capacity of the village by nearly one hundred percent, but since acceptable population densities were falling at this time, it is by no means certain that either employment at the factory or village population really increased to this extent. Between one and two hundred people were employed in the factory throughout its history, as the printing and dyeing processes were by no means labour intensive. In the 1871 Census John Pullar junior claimed to employ 283 people, but this was at both the Ashfield and Kierfield factories. My contemporary informants described Ashfield as always having employed about 130, so it seems unlikely that the

92 expansion of housing at the turn of the century was because of major expansion in employment.

One hundred and ten years of Ashfield attracted little attention from the world outside — the building of both factory and village square in 1866; the village expansion of 1898; some additional agricultural land purchased and the building of a new housing block, the Clachan, for agricultural workers just before the First World War; the selling of both factories and the village by Pullars at the close of the Second World War, with the continuation of the Ashfield printworks and village under new ownership for the next thirty years, now printing on synthetic fabrics instead of cotton. Not until the British Silk Dyeing Company in its turn closed the factory, and sold it and the village in 1976 to a local builder, did Ashfield reach the front page of even the local newspaper. Perhaps because it just quietly and successfully fulfilled the functions for which it was intended by its owners and residents, was neither a first, last, biggest or best industrial village, it has never attracted the attention of a historian.

The factory is now owned by a company making equipment for the oil industry, and most of the houses have been restored and let to people working elsewhere, so the tightknit community around the mill is no more. What was it like to live in such a village? Fortunately a few people who lived and worked there before the Second World War are still amongst its residents, and their evidence together with a few news items in the local newspapers together allow us to reconstruct a picture of life in the village.

Ashfield was a real and distinctive community, with its Angling Club, Band of Hope, Boys Brigade, Cycling Club, Orchestral Society and Quoiting Club all periodically submitting their news to the *Stirling Journal.* Its identity was created by its geographical isolation and shared employment, as all the village housing was owned by the factory. It had no school — children walked to Kinbuck, no Church, and no shop — although the village hallkeeper did sell sweets and cigarettes. The parish church at Dunblane set up a Sunday School in the village hall, which most of the village children attended. The factory manager seems to have been Sunday School Superintendent throughout the period of Pullars' ownership, a coincidence noted in many other factory villages.

Attempts by the other necessary Dunblane institution to gain a foothold in the village were less successful. The largest retailing organisation in Dunblane was the Co-operative Society, and the Pullars, who were active supporters of the Liberal Party — renaming Ashfield Square as Gladstone Square early in the present century —

refused permission for the Co-op to open a shop in the village. However one of the factory's carts did go to the Co-op in Dunblane every Thursday afternoon to collect the grocery orders for the entire village!

Gas lighting from the Dunblane gasworks was used both in the factory and for street lights on the Square from the beginning, but gas was not available in the houses, and oil lamps and candles were the only source of domestic lighting in Ashfield until the North of Scotland Hydro Electric Board brought electricity to the village in 1948. Yet with good working conditions and low rents, e.g. 1s 6d (7½p) per week for two rooms in 1946, it seems to have been a contented community. 'Pullars wouldn't employ anyone without a collar and tie', I was informed. But it was different with the new owners after the Second World War, 'Anyone from Barlinnie could come here then.' I asked what happened if there was a dispute between neighbours during the Pullars' period of ownership, did not the fact that neighbours worked together, and landlords were also employers, make for difficulties? 'You just went straight to Mr Muir' (the factory manager in the 20's and 30's) I was told, 'Their word was law.' Why, I asked, did he say 'their' of Mr Muir's decisions — did the Pullars involve themselves too? 'No, they left everything to Mr Muir'. Yet clearly in the minds of my informants, Mr Muir was identified absolutely with the company and the owners.

Work discipline and social control figure prominently in the development of our industrial society — in small factory villages like Ashfield they are clearly mutually reinforcing. Where houses and community go with the job in modern eyes much of the individual's freedom is lost. Yet my informants spoke warmly of their community, and showed me proudly a book each employee was given in 1901, and which had been handed down in the family since. It was a memorial tribute to Frederick Pullar, whose death in a skating accident on Airthrey Loch had robbed the Keirfield factory of an able manager, and Laurence Pullar, the then owner, of his only son. The *Stirling Journal* (22nd February, 1901; 5th July, 1901) relates how all the staff of both Keirfield and Ashfield attended the funeral. Now we have no means of knowing whether this was because of love, respect, curiosity, or compulsion: their lives were too tied to their employers' for full freedom of action to exist. Yet there is some evidence that these bonds were recognised as mutual, the interdependence of both owners and employees, for after the funeral Laurence Pullar gave every employee not only the book listing his dead son's achievements, but also the sum of ten pounds. This gift, to about three hundred employees, on the death of his only son,

94 gives the term 'paternalism' a rather fuller meaning than we usually attribute to it.

A village of 51 houses stands ten kilometres to the north of Stirling, surrounded by green fields. It is at present being restored by a local builder, and at the end of the village is a factory making equipment for the North Sea oil industry. Why is it there, between a river too shallow to navigate and a railway line in too deep a cutting ever to have had a station? There are scores of similar settlements all over Scotland with little or no written history, attracting no attention from the world outside in their heyday, and with few to lament their passing unless they possess exceptional visual charm. Yet if we do not before the memories are dead record the little that is known about such places, they might one day become as inexplicable as the brochs. But if we do try to gather such records together we will be able to generalise about the industrial transformation of Britain with greater confidence, and occasionally gain new insights into a very distinctive type of settlement in the highland margins of eighteenth and nineteenth century Britain, the Factory Village.

Figure 2. The 1909 disposition showing the 'square' development plan for property 2.089

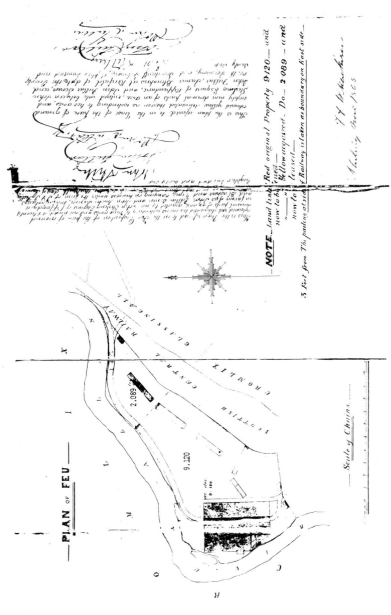

Figure 1 The 1865 disposition — showing the leased northern part 2.089, and the main feued area 9.120

96   EDUCATION IN BOTHKENNAR PARISH IN THE TIME OF THE REV. WILLIAM NIMMO, HISTORIAN OF STIRLINGSHIRE

Andrew Bain

INTRODUCTION

Some initial explanation is due to the reader regarding both the scope of this contribution and the form in which it appears. The substance of what follows was first presented in 1979 as one of a series of annual talks given in Bothkennar Parish Church to mark the connection of Stirlingshire's first historian with the Parish, where he was minister from 1765 until 1782. The series of talks was initiated in 1978 by the present minister, the Rev. W. B. Maclaren, whose plan it is that each speaker should consider one aspect of Nimmo's times. In the present case this was education.

For the historian who is well versed in the development of education in Central Scotland there will be nothing very new in what follows, for Bothkennar is representative of the geographical area and the historical times rather than remarkable in any major way, but the details themselves may be of some interest, and perhaps the argued view of the general context into which those details have been put may lead to some useful discussion.

THE GENERAL CONTEXT

The years from 1765 to 1782 were not highly significant years in education, either in the Parish of Bothkennar or in the Central Lowlands of Scotland as a whole. Perhaps they were in parts of the Highlands, or in some of the new academies that were springing up, but not in Bothkennar. The reason they were not in any way outstanding or unusual was simply that the development of education in Bothkennar in the second half of the 18th century fell quite clearly between two periods of tremendous upheaval and social change. The first was the Protestant Reformation, which spread throughout the Scottish Lowlands in the 16th and 17th centuries, altering the whole way in which schooling was looked at. The second was the Industrial Revolution, which began in a sense on the very doorstep of the Parish, and which increasingly throughout the 19th century altered the whole basis of Lowland society from a rural to an industrialised economy. As a result of that 19th century change education was never quite the same again, and education in

Bothkennar in Nimmo's time therefore falls quite clearly between **97**
these two epoch-making events in our national history. Because this is
so, it is proposed to look at some aspects of education in Bothkennar
that are recorded in the parish registers against the much wider
background of these two great changes: The Protestant Reformation
that came before Nimmo's time, and the Industrial Revolution that
followed so quickly upon it. The events recorded as parish history
only make sense to us two hundred years later if we look at them in
this way.

We therefore begin with a very brief consideration of what the
Protestant Reformation meant in Scottish education, of what that
first great burst of reforming zeal meant for schools and schooling.
The older (Roman Catholic) Church had depended upon the priest as
an intermediary between God and sinful men. When at the
Reformation the priest was removed as a go-between, and men were
encouraged to have direct contact *with* God, and to have direct
responsibility *to* God, it was necessary to find a new source of
guidance for them. The Bible became that source. But knowing the
Bible for oneself meant being able to read it for oneself, and being
able to read eventually meant schools and teachers. So we find in the
educational programmes of European Reformers like Luther and
Calvin, and in the educational plans of Scotsmen like John Knox and
his contemporaries, provision for what we would nowadays call
universal literacy. Wherever especially the Calvinistic model of a
Reformed Church sprang up — in Europe, in America, in Scotland —
so in time a school and a schoolmaster became associated with it.
Reading the Bible in order to save one's soul led to schools and to
schooling in a direct and most positive way. Additionally, since the
Protestant Church was essentially a reforming Church, those who
planned the Reformation in Scotland aimed to change the whole of a
corrupt society for the better, and the two instruments through
which they intended to do so were the pulpit and the school. In this
scheme the school's functions were twofold. First of all, in order that
a moral, Bible-reading flock should be created in every parish, all
children were to be taught the rudiments of reading, writing,
arithmetic, Bible and the Catechism. Secondly, in order that leaders
should be found to continue the reformation of society, the most
able boys were sifted out and taken on eventually to university, to
return as the ministers, doctors, lawyers and schoolmasters that
continuing improvement needed. No academic talent was to be
wasted in farm or field work. No father was to keep an able child
from further education. Children who were too poor to attend school
were assisted to do so by the Kirk Session, and those who needed
support at university were given it by the Presbytery.

98   At this point it is necessary to keep very much in mind that the society was an almost entirely rural one; it was a slow-moving society; it was a society without our large cities, with few large towns, and even with comparatively few villages; it comprised on the whole, a scattered and a sparse population based in agriculture. It was a society terribly dependent upon a reasonable harvest, and very quickly reduced to widespread hunger, disease, misery and death by a bad one. It was for the reform and running of such a society that the Reformers drew up their plans for one kirk and one school in every parish, and in such a society that they intended the school to be an efficient instrument for changing the lives of people. The basic ideal was to change society — and then to hold that reformed society static and unchanging over the years. Bothkennar in Nimmo's day reflected the static period which followed the far-reaching changes of the Scottish Reformation: it was a late 18th century Lowland Scottish country parish with its one kirk and its one school, long established in just the way that the 16th and 17th century Reformers had wanted. It was a parish that had survived some local difficulties associated with early 18th century Episcopacy, and had moved on beyond the changes of the first great burst of reform into times that can only seem to us — with our awareness of the Industrial Revolution to come — somewhat humdrum and repetitive in educational, as in other, matters. It was a parish that, by the evidence of its own kirk records, would seem to have been providing fairly effectively the kind of schooling that the Reformers thought was necessary to keep rural society reformed. This is the context in which are placed the details that have been recorded of education in Bothkennar in William Nimmo's time. These years constitute a period that falls right between two great changes, managing to embody the ideals of the first in a rather quiet way before the onset of the second began to disrupt first the economy and then the society of the Forth and Clyde Valley.

EDUCATIONAL PROVISION AND SCHOOL LIFE

Into this general context can be put some of the details of the schooling provided in Bothkennar in Nimmo's times: details of what school life was like both for the masters and for the pupils. This can be done by drawing upon the surviving minutes of the Parish itself, but now and again, where these are silent, by looking at what is known of surrounding parishes like Larbert, Airth, and Falkirk that would not be greatly different from Bothkennar in the 18th century. In considering these details of school life in a post-Reformation parish, it has to be kept in mind that we are dealing with the educational needs of a very small entirely rural and agricultural area just under 2½ x 2½ km; a parish with between only 600 and 700 souls scattered throughout it; a parish that in the eyes of the Reformers could very readily be served by one kirk and one school at a fairly central point within it to which both young and old could travel even in winter; a parish in which in the 1790s there were 133 children under the age of ten, and therefore probably less than half of that number of school age.

From the very earliest entries in the extant Bothkennar Kirk Session Records it is quite clear that the Parish was being provided with both a school and a schoolmaster in almost the way that the Reformers had wished. By at least 1725 – some 40 years before Nimmo – there were in existence a schoolhouse and a schoolmaster's house and yard or garden, and the only difficulty seemed to be that instead of the Heritors having provided a school – as the Act of 1696 required – the Kirk Session had in fact paid for it out of the poor's fund. This wasn't an uncommon situation, but in 1725 the Session made it quite clear that the Heritors – absent or not – would now have to meet their legal obligations, and so the schoolmaster was told 'to flitt' from all his accommodation as a means of putting pressure on the Heritors. A stent (assessment) was quickly agreed in order to repay the Session; eventually the original outlay of £140 Scots (about £12 Sterling) was met; and from then on all seems to have been well. Periodical repairs were met by the Session, but only until the Heritors paid up; and occasionally in the 1760s and 1790s the Session itself met in what seems to have been a school in good repair (The Register, various dates 1725-92).

An 18th century building had little resemblance to a school like Larbert High, or even Carronshore or Carron Primary – not even the old ones – but was something much more modest. It is unfortunate that there are no surviving pictures or plans; only the detail that the cost of the school was £140 Scots (ibid 9th October 1727). But it would be a not unreasonable guess that it had one not very large classroom, with living accommodation for the master up above. If so, the whole two-storey building would probably not have exceeded a quarter of the present Bothkennar Church in size, and since it is recorded that thatch was bought in 1726 (ibid 3rd October 1726), it is reasonable to suppose that the roof was at that time thatched, and perhaps leaked occasionally during a stormy winter. The floor might have been earthen, and covered by rushes or straw collected by the children – a custom common in those days. The desks would not be individual seats as now, but long, common, wooden benches shared by many pupils.

100   We know that the schoolmaster had a house as well as a school
(ibid 9th April 1725). In that he was fortunate, since under the Act
of 1696 the Heritors needed legally to provide only a building for a
school. The same Act also entitled the master to a legal salary of
between 100 and 200 merks (a merk was a silver coin worth 13½d
Sterling). Again the records tell us that by at least 1725 a salary of
100 merks was agreed (ibid 9th July 1725). This was the sum still
being paid in the 1790s, after Nimmo's time, though by then the
basic salary of 100 merks was being supplemented voluntarily by
some of the Heritors in an attempt to attract good masters (The
Statistical Account 1794). It is perhaps not easy for us to appreciate
in these times of annual salary increases of £500, that between 1696
and 1803, in a full century of gradually rising prices, schoolmasters
saw no change at all in their legal salaries. For them there was no
Houghton, and no Clegg. Like their contemporaries elsewhere in
central Scotland, the schoolmasters of Bothkennar therefore sought
to augment their salaries in as many ways as they could. Thus we
know from the records that almost always the master was appointed
session clerk immediately after his acceptance as schoolmaster by the
Heritors and the Presbytery, and that throughout the 18th century he
received from the Session £12.12.0 Scots (or £1.1.0 Sterling)
annually as clerk (The Register 10th November 1723, 25th May
1759, 4th June 1794). He was also normally appointed precentor,
and the records again and again register his receipt of 5/— or 6/—
Sterling for his services at Communion (e.g. ibid 26th May 1728,
16th December 1793). He shared in collections made at baptisms; he
received fees for recording burials; he sought payment for acting as
treasurer (e.g. ibid 1st June 1726, 12th September 1793) — all these
were small but welcome additions to his legal income.

One source of income that he had very much under his own
control of course, since it varied with his academic reputation, was
schollage, or pupils' fees. What these amounted to is exemplified in
the recorded appointment of Mr. James Izat, Preacher of the Gospel,
as schoolmaster in 1773, when the Heritors and Session on 12th
February

'did and hereby do appoint, That in time Coming the
School-Wages Should be as follows, Viz, The teaching of English &
Writing one Shilling & Sixpence Sterl; per Quarter, The Teaching
of Arithmetic and the Latin tongue, Two Shillings & Sixpence
Sterl: per Qr. — And Further they appoint that the School-wages
Shall be paid upon the entry of the Children to the School, Either
Monthly or Quarterly as the Parents please, as the meeting are
perswaded this will tend to the interest of the Children.'

Some pupils of course could not pay, and for them the Session again and again recorded outlay from its funds towards their support as poor scholars (e.g. ibid 24th January 1731, 14th May 1798).

All these sources of basic and additional income still added up to a relatively small annual sum: about £20 Sterling in the early 1790s, at a time when farm servants could earn about £10 Sterling per year, and the grave-digger received 1/6d (7½p) for digging a grave and ringing the funeral bell (The Statistical Account 1794; The Register 12th February 1773). As the Reverend Mr. Dickson, successor to William Nimmo, wrote in this Old Statistical Account

'It is much to be wished that, in this age of liberality and improvement, something were done for the encouragement of schoolmasters, many of whom, having families to support, must often be straitend to obtain even the necessaries of life.'

This sometimes meant that parish schoolmasters did not stay overlong in a post, restlessly moving on in search of greater emoluments, but Bothkennar seems to have been reasonably congenial, since during the 17 years of Nimmo's charge — 1765 to 1782 — there were only three masters, possibly four if he inherited a year at the end of John Russell's time. These were as follows

James Anderson, who served 6 years, and apparently died in office;

James Izat, who served less than 1 year, and who probably left to become a minister, as was not uncommon;

John Donaldson, who spent 12 years in his post.

(The Register, 16th July 1766, 13th December 1772, 12th February 1773, 15th January 1774, 14th May 1786)

Less than well paid the masters probably were, and looking for a pulpit some may have been, but the pattern I have described does not suggest that Bothkennar was a place to be avoided during William Nimmo's time.

So much then for the school and its masters. What of school life? The Statistical Account tells us that there were about 60 pupils at the school during this period, but what their exact ages were we cannot say. Since, however, it does tell us that the masters of Bothkennar were appointed to teach reading, writing, arithmetic, geography, Latin and Greek, and since we know that in general rural children at this time tended to spend only two to four years on the basics before leaving, it would seem likely that, apart from one or two pupils learning Latin and Greek, the pupils for the most past would be below twelve years of age, probably well below twelve. For the majority, most of the long school day would be spent in having the rudiments drilled into them, often by the assistance of

102 punishment that was considered both a useful means of controlling a large class of 60 pupils, and also an accepted means of preparing children for adult life here on earth and for eternal life hereafter. Although we no longer accept it, in Nimmo's day the belief was widespread that in all its elements — in management, in organisation, and in methods — education should be completely in accord with a Calvinistic interpretation of human destiny.

Since such drilling in the rudiments was a full-time job whose demands had to be reconciled with the needs of those few pupils studying Latin and Greek, the master in Bothkennar was sometimes allowed the assistance of a junior master, or doctor, who was responsible for English reading and writing. The Kirk Session, not the Heritors, paid him, and the records show fluctuating payments like £24 Scots per annum in 1727, £12 in 1736, and again £24 just before 1776, while the doctor appointed in that year could not be promised 'more than the session's circumstances would admit of', however worthy he was, and however many of a family he had to support. Throughout the period, the doctor was appointed only during the Session's pleasure — a very common arrangement (The Register 2nd September 1727, 17th October 1736, 22nd July 1776). Even when such a division of duties in the supervision of 60 children of many ages in one room could be paid for, their schooling must have been a physically cramped, emotionally desiccated, imaginatively limited kind of experience. The life of the school was teacher-centred, rule-bounded, highly disciplined, readily punished, based upon drill techniques and the encouragement of brief but correct answers. Influenced by the form and the certainty of the Catechism, there was no such thing in those days as a good wrong answer. It was a schoolroom experience that prepared children for the static society envisaged by the Reformers, a society in which the adults they were so soon to become were overseen by a Kirk Session that was devoted in a thoroughgoing Scottish way to the human potential for good. The experience of the schoolroom reflected the experience of 18th century adult life: it was hard; it was earnest; it was disciplined; it was closely related to an awareness of social possibility that was necessarily restricted by contemporary economic development, and to an awareness of human destiny that was almost equally restricted by the theology of the times. It was not competent to deal with social change; it was not designed to consider social change. And yet we are now aware that it was fundamental social change that was just over the horizon from Nimmo's time.

Everything that we know of school life in Bothkennar in Nimmo's day suggests that it did not foresee, and that it could not foresee, the vast economic, social and intellectual upheavals that were to stem from the opening of Carron Iron Works in 1759, and from the beginning of mining soon afterwards in Bothkennar Parish itself. These developments produced changes in the number and distribution of population in the Parish: the traditional 500 to 600 souls became 821 in 1811, and 905 in 1831 (The New Statistical Account 1845). A new school costing £600 Sterling was built in 1830 to cope with the increase (ibid). These developments also produced changes in the way that the claims of a parish church were looked at, as the Reverend Mr Caw's references (ibid) to the absence of religious observance in local miners made clear

'Their wages are high, and the greater part is spent on the Saturday and Sabbath in public houses, which contributes exceedingly to make them inattentive to the ordinances of religion.'

They produced changes in social habits, so that a boatman or a barber going about his trade on Sundays could no longer be tried by the Session (The Register 12th February 1727, 20th December 1746, 15th September 1760, 14th and 21st August 1768). They eventually produced the changes in education that led to the School Board schools e.g. in Carron, Carronshore, and Larbert. These were schools that fitted into a system that was designed to train efficient workmen for a secular 19th century society rather than to prepare a moral flock to fit into the Godly Commonwealth envisaged by the 16th and 17th century Scottish Reformers; and these were schools that could at least begin to provide for the greater opportunities that the twentieth century has offered to the upward social mobility that Scottish academic talent has always seized upon — almost in an Old Testament way — as outward proof of high personal worth.

In retrospect, the period spanned by William Nimmo's ministry stands in education almost peacefully between the first great period of reformation that endeavoured to produce a system of parish schools in Scotland, and the beginnings of the dynamic, industrial, commercial, secular outlook that has produced the present. It stands between the first phase of a system designed to produce a Godly Commonwealth and the first phase of a system designed to produce an efficient industrialised state.

SOME POSSIBLE CONCLUSIONS

Having said all this, what is one now to conclude about education in Bothkennar in Nimmo's time? I should like to make five simple points.

First, although by comparison this was a quiet, conservative period

104 in the history of education in Bothkennar, it was also a well-run period in which the Reformers' ideals were being maintained; if problems arose, then they were clearly met: they did not develop into any kind of breakdown of the accepted system; and there was evident in the Parish a habit of vigilance about what had been achieved by the Reformation, a vigilance that was expressed in the form of a warning in the Register of 5th January 1779 against the dangers of Jesuit education in the kingdom

'That indulgence granted to Popish Priests and Jesuits to keep Schools and take upon them the Education or Government of Youth in this Realm is too certain a method of tainting many of the rising generation with principles, not only opposite to the Simplicity of the Gospel, but pernicious to the Natural and Civil Interests of Mankind.'

Secondly, this desire to maintain the system can be seen to have been both expressed and working in so many ways. There was a schoolmaster's house years before its provision was required by law. Some of the Heritors voluntarily supplemented the basic legal salary of 100 merks. The Kirk Session regularly paid the master for poor scholars, and provided for an English doctor whenever this was financially possible. There was no need for adventure schools, or for any school other than the legal one. All of these suggest the efficient oversight of, and care for, education in an 18th century parish.

Thirdly, since we don't have any direct record of the pressure that was needed to maintain the inherited system of schooling in Bothkennar, we don't know to what extent William Nimmo himself was required to exert such pressure between 1765 and 1782. But to put the point rather negatively, had he been the kind of minister who did not care, or who did not exert vigilance in relation to what had been achieved, the results of his failure would certainly have been recorded — as they were in many another parish where the minister's supervision was lax. Although it was the presbytery that had the legal right to redress moral or academic misdemeanour, it was most often in fact the minister and the session that exerted close day-to-day supervision over both master and school. William Nimmo himself seems not always to have enjoyed good health, but the absence of recorded educational transgression suggests a close and careful sessional oversight in Bothkennar.

Fourthly, I don't feel that too much can be made of the point that Bothkennar did not foresee the future, that in Nimmo's time it merely went its own humdrum parochial way, unaware of the social and educational implications of industrial change. We have grown up in a century of change, and in a century that plans for change as something that is inevitable; but the social philosphy of the post-Reformation period was fundamentally different: it was rather to avoid further change, since change was considered a falling away from the highest ideals of the Reformers. Both the ministers and the schoolmasters of those times — however able in other respects — were raised in such totally different habits of thought from our own about change in society.

Finally, and not unrelated to the previous point, it is fairly certain that William Nimmo would never have said, as was recorded of the Revered James Buchanan in the Register of the Presbytery of Dumbarton for July-August 1690, that

'it was not needful for the common people to learn to read and pray; it belonged only to the ministers and not the people, and that it was never good for the land since there were so many scholars in it.'

Had Nimmo been of that mind, education in Bothkennar in his times would not have maintained the standards, and the knowledge, and the habits of industrious application and honesty that, as T. C. Smout so rightly says, at least prepared Scotsmen in some measure for the future — prepared them to take advantage of the ethic of their Protestant Reformation background in adapting very quickly to the new demands of an industrialised and commercialised age when it did come.

So it may be said, in conclusion, that the years of Nimmo's ministry from 1765 until 1782 were a quiet time in the educational history of Bothkennar, a period between two events of much greater social and educational import. Yet they constituted also a period essential to the maintenance of the highest achievements of one event, and were not entirely lacking in unconscious preparation for the other. Nimmo's times in the history of education in Bothkennar were true to the only criteria that those times knew, and they kept faith with the best of the past as they understood it. One cannot ask for very much more.

A

GENERAL HISTORY

OF

STIRLINGSHIRE;

CONTAINING

An Account of the Ancient Monuments, and moſt
Important and Curious Tranſactions in that Shire,
from the Roman Invaſion of Scotland, to the Pre-
ſent Times;

WITH THE

NATURAL HISTORY

OF THE SHIRE.

By WILLIAM NIMMO,
Miniſter of Bothkennar.

Illuſtrated with a large Map of the Shire, from an actual Survey.

Hic acies certare ſolebant.

EDINBURGH:

Printed for WILLIAM CREECH,
And ſold by T. CADELL, London.

M,DCC,LXXVII.

SOME BACKGROUND NOTES ON WILLIAM NIMMO (1733-1782)   **107**
THE FIRST HISTORIAN OF STIRLINGSHIRE

William B. Maclaren and Andrew Bain

The purpose of these notes is not to review in any way the
History of Stirlingshire (Nimmo 1777) that begins with the pages
illustrated in Figures 1 and 2; nor is it to attempt to assess anew the
historiographical significance of Nimmo's eighteenth century work. It
is much more modestly to provide a few details of local background
to the period that he spent in the parish referred to in the general
description and the dedication of his book.

Nimmo completed both his *History* and his short life in the Parish
of Bothkennar, and although it would now be difficult for the casual
visitor to arrive easily at his burial place — since neither the National
Trust for Scotland nor the Local Authority has yet seen fit to erect a
single signpost to it — the grave itself is clearly enough marked within
the Kirkyard of Bothkennar, and the stone carries full testimony to
his pastor's life, as well as to the death of his wife, who did not long
survive him. In modernised spelling, and with small conjectural
additions made necessary by the effects of weathering, their
interment is recorded as follows:
'Beneath this stone is interred the Body of the Rev'd William
Nimmo late Minister of the Gospel at Bothkennar a man in life
most justly esteemed and at his death sincerely regretted by all
who knew him especially by the people under his charge. In
distress he was ever cheerful and resigned till having finished his
course he fell asleep in Jesus on the 9th of October, 1782 in the
49th year of his age and 18th of his Ministry. Blessed are the
Dead that Die in the Lord &c. Rev. 14, 13, Mark the perfect &c.
Ps 37.37.'
In this grave lies the body of Mrs Jane Jamieson his spouse who
died June 1783 aged 45 years.
Be ye also ready.'
Both these records of Nimmo, the completion of his *History* in
1777 and his burial in 1782, refer essentially to his last five years,
but his connection with Bothkennar spanned the major part of his
adult life, and links with the county which he served so well as
minister and historian go even farther back, being recorded as early as
12th April 1758, when the Presbytery of Stirling 'made choice of Mr
William Nimmo to be their Clerk'. In a period when parishes were
difficult to come by, he was still at that time a probationer, and
although one of the candidates for the neighbouring parish of Airth

To his G R A C E

W I L L I A M

DUKE of MONTROSE,

&c. &c. &c.

And other

NOBLEMEN and GENTLEMEN

Having intereſt in the Shire of Stirling;

The following

GENERAL HISTORY of that Shire

Iſ inſcribed,

With much reſpect, by

Their moſt humble

And

Moſt obedient Servant

WILLIAM NIMMO.

BOTHKENNAR, }
May 1. 1777. }

in 1762 (ibid 13th October 1762), he seems to have remained so **109** until 1765/66, when he was called from St. Ninians to Bothkennar (ibid December 1765 — April 1766).

The details of the process of appointment are interesting in themselves. In December 1765 Nimmo's presentation to the Parish was granted by the then patron, Captain George Middleton of Lethamdolls (ibid 18th December 1765), and was approved in turn by the votes of the heritors and elders (ibid 22nd January 1766). The Presbytery of Stirling, finding matters regular and agreed thus far, thereupon prescribed for Mr Nimmo's trials 'an Exercise and addition on Gen(esis) 49, 10 — The sceptre shall not depart from Judah nor a lawgiver from between his feet till Shiloh come'. This, together with an Exegesis on Christus verus Deus, was to be delivered at the next meeting of the Presbytery (ibid 22nd January 1766).

In February 1766 both of these tasks were performed before the members at their meeting in Stirling, and were 'sustained as parts of his trials'. He was then 'for further trials' set (a) a lecture on the conversion of the Ethipian Eunuch; (b) a sermon on Psalm 30,5,

'For his anger endureth but a moment; in his favour is life: weeping may endure for a night, but joy cometh in the morning'

and (c) an examination on the Greek and Hebrew languages (ibid 19th February 1766). In April he duly delivered his sermon, was examined in the languages, and 'went through all the other parts of his trials to the satisfaction of the presbytery' (ibid 2nd April 1766).

On the day appointed for his ordination at Bothkennar — the 30th of April — no impediment was put forward in response to the three calls made from the church door as to whether 'any had objections to the life and doctrine of Mr William Nimmo'. An appropriate sermon was then preached by the Moderator of the Presbytery, Mr Robert Ure (who incidentally had been the successful candidate for Airth in 1762), hands were laid on, the right hand of fellowship was extended, and William Nimmo finally became the recognised minister of the parish that was to sustain him for the remainder of his life (ibid 30th April 1766).

Having thus secured his charge, he married Jane Jamieson on the 29th of October 1766, and in due course this union gave birth to a family of seven children, three boys and four girls (Fasti Ecclesiae Scoticannae - Parish of Bothkennar). Such an increase in his responsibilities caused the new minister to re-consider the sources of his income, and since Bothkennar was the smallest pre-Reformation parish in Scotland, with a stipend commensurate with its size, Nimmo represented to the Presbytery in 1769 that his parish income was too small, 'being only nine hundred Merks Scots'. He intimated that

'he intended to begin a process agt. the Heritors of said parish for

110   an augmentation of his stipend and craved that the presbytery would concur with him therein'. The members 'having heard & considered the above petition and judging it highly reasonable, did & hereby do grant the desire thereof and concur with the said Mr Nimmo in a process of augmentation before the court of Session and also recommend it to him to set about it as soon as possible' (Presbytery of Stirling 8th November 1769).

Nimmo's desire for an increase seems to have been met, for he remained at Bothkennar until his death thirteen years later, and could apparently afford to give up the position of Clerk to the Presbytery of Stirling during the following year (ibid 20th September and 21st November 1970).

Of these thirteen years we do not gather many details from local church records, but we must suppose that he was busy with the writing of his *History of Stirlingshire* and with increasing commitments to his growing family, born at regular intervals between 1767 and 1780.

Sadly, it is of his last months that we can gather a great deal more. For example, the sederunt of meetings of the Presbytery showed up his sparse attendances during the period 1780-82, and on the 12th of October 1782 the Presbytery met at Bothkennar for his interment. Characteristically for a group that always had to consider the ongoing business of the present and had to make plans for the continuing and regular preaching of the Word, its record for that meeting is divided between a recognition of the late incumbent's worthiness as a pastor and a recognition of the need to fill his pulpit the following day,

'At Bothkennar the Twelfth Day of October One thousand Seven hundred and Eighty-two; Which Day the Presbytery of Stirling being met and constituted immediately after the Interment of the late Mr William Nimmo Minister of this Parish. Sederunt, Mr Muschet Modr. Messrs. Oswald, Ure and Buchanan Ministers. Mr Buchanan was chosen Clerk pro tempore.

The taking into Consideration that this parish is now become vacant by the Death of their late worthy pastor, proceeded to appoint the following Ministers to supply the vacant Parish till next Meeting of Presbytery, viz . . . . . .'

The accounts book of the Treasurer of the Kirk of Bothkennar tells us a bit more about the duration and increasing severity of Nimmo's condition in brief incidental references to his intermittent absences from the pulpit throughout the months of June, July, August and September of 1782, and in an entry on 13th October that finally records the death of 'our late Worthy Pastor'

'June 16th   No sermon Mr Nimmo being Indisposed

June 23rd	No sermon Mr Nimmo being at the Goat Whey	
June 30th	No sermon Mr Nimmo being absent	
July 7th	No sermon Mr Nimmo being absent	
July 21st	No sermon Mr Nimmo being absent as above	
July 28th	No sermon Mr Nimmo being Still Indispos'd	
Aug. 4th	No sermon Mr Nimmo being indispos'd	
Sept. 1st	No sermon — Mr Nimmo being in distress	
Sept. 15th	No sermon Mr Nimmo being in distress	
Sept. 29th	No sermon Mr Nimmo being still in distress	
Oct. 13th	Mr Oswald preach'd and declared the Kirk Vacant by the Death of our late Worthy Pastor Mr Nimmo who departed this Life on the ninth Current . . . . .'	

The full poignancy of the situation during the four months covered so laconically by the Treasurer's entries perhaps only emerges when we put his record side by side with the Register of the Kirk Session covering the same period. Like the record of almost any other session of the time, it is replete with the details of a seemingly interminable succession of paternity cases — for many years now the business of secular courts — and it is perhaps sufficient to quote an entry that refers to one of the meetings that Nimmo was fit enough to attend.

'Bothkennar 10th August 1782. The Session being met and Constitute Sedt. Minr. & Elders Janet Miller having been called Compeared & being interrogate if she adhered to her former declaration that Robt. David was the Father of the Child she had brought forth in April last, She Answered yes he was, Robert David being called & Compeared by virtue of a Summons from Mr Bennet Minr in Polmont & being interrogate as to what was laid to his charge, he denied his being father of Janet Miller's child but owned his being in Mrs Gaff's house & drinking with her there & before this meeting he had heard she was with child, he confessed likewise he saw & spoke with her on the evening of the Maidlen fair of Linlithgow, and had spoke with her many other times, the parties being removed, & the Session taking this affair into Consideration are of Opinion that from the said Robert David's acknowledging his seeing and speaking with Janet Miller on the said fair night & his being with her in Mrs Gaff's house & their drinking together, & that after he had heard she was with child; these circumstances are presumptions against him therefore cannot Assoilzie him but for the present must leave the affair till providence shall give them more light how to proceed therein. Concluded with prayer. The above was the last time Mr Nimmo kept Session'.

In response to the juxtaposition of the matter under consideration

112 and that final sentence, it is immediately tempting in a different age and with a different way of looking at things, to dwell with a degree of sadness upon a picture of the talented, terminally ill minister having to find his way through the details of such cases. Even for *any* age there may be a perenially sad aspect to such involvement. Yet, for eighteenth century ministers like Nimmo, this kind of procedure was inseparable from the maintenance of moral and administrative standards that had come down largely unchanged from the Reformation, and their strong sense of duty must have helped them — especially in sickness — to maintain these standards. The world of the Scottish country parish in Nimmo's time was still in great part the intellectual world of the sixteenth century Scottish Reformation, with a supportive framework of Reformation beliefs, Reformation values, Reformation social habits, and Reformation forms of local government and administration.

And yet for all that commitment to older patterns of thought, Nimmo was apparently aware of the beginning of some of the changes that we now take so much for granted, for in his *History* he expressed himself at some length as follows:

'It is an opinion generally adopted, that, in ancient times, this whole tract was covered by the waters of the neighbouring Frith, which, by some unknown revolution, hath contracted its channel. Beds of oisters and shells of every kind, are found within a few feet of the surface. There, however, are not always certain indications of the land having made a part of the ocean, since they have often been found in places most distant from the sea, in the very bowels of the earth, and on tops of mountains. There are phaenomena, which, in innumerable instances, philosophy cannot with any degree of satisfaction, account for, without admitting the truth of the information conveyed by the sacred scriptures, concerning the universal deluge, which the Supreme Being brought upon the earth, in the days of Noah to destroy the wicked inhabitants thereof.

Nevertheless, the discovery of different sorts of shells, and other relicts of the sea, in greater abundance than is to be met with in other places, together with the low situation, which is generally but a few feet above the level of the water, and which, in many parts, would still be covered in high tides, if it was not protected from the rage of that fluid by dikes or mounds, raised by human industry, afford a high degree of probability, that the tract we are surveying had been overflown in ages much later than the universal deluge, and that the ocean hath there lost a part of its ancient possessions.

It is certain, that, by the revolutions of that element, dry land hath been lost in one quarter of the globe and gained in another. Earth and sea appear to wage a reciprocal war, and have at sundry times obtained local victories over each other. Banks of sand at present cover cities, which were once celebrated sea-ports; and cities now lift their spires to the skies, upon shores once covered by the waves. Upon the retreat of the fluid from those parts, it must have expanded on some other shore; for, philosophy instructs us, that the vast waters of the ocean are necessary to preserve the equilibrium of the globe, and, therefore, can admit of no great addition or diminution; hence, when they retire from one shore, they must necessarily incroach upon another' (Nimmo 1777 p429-431)

Here Nimmo showed himself aware of some of the intellectual difficulties that were to become much more fully defined and demarcated during the following century, and it is tantalising to consider what the content of his sermons might have been, three-quarters of the way through a century which was organisationally and administratively little different from that of the Reformation two hundred years before, and yet one in which minds like his own were open to the registering of impressions and the making of observations that gave rise to the enquiries that followed much more obviously in the intellectual ferment of the nineteenth century. Just as it is tantalising to consider what might have been the contents of the library of an eighteenth century country minister whose mind clearly ranged beyond the confines of both the time and the place of his ministry in Bothkennar Parish.

But such speculation is not the purpose of these notes, and we shall be well satisfied if in some small way attention has been drawn both to the life and work of Stirlingshire's first historian, and to the regrettable fact that the way to his resting place in Bothkennar Churchyard remains unmarked to the present time.

114 THE OLD SCOTTISH POOR LAW: THE PRACTICE OF STIRLINGSHIRE, 1790-1845

D. E. Gladstone
University of Exeter

The Scottish system of poor relief had its origins in legislation passed in the sixteenth century. Its principles remained relatively unaltered until formally amended by legislation in 1845. But in the interim, as Rosalind Mitchison (1974) has shown, there was considerable diversity of administrative operation between areas of the country and changes in practice over time. By the period immediately preceding the Poor Law Amendment (Scotland) Act of 1845 the variation, as Levitt and Smout (1979 p173) describe it, was

'from a non existent or rudimentary poor law in the North west to a highly organised English poor law in the south east'

Such a diversity in operation underlines the need for studies of local practice.

Drawing on a variety of national and local sources it is the purpose of this paper to describe the system of poor relief as it operated in the parishes of Stirlingshire between the end of the eighteenth century and the middle of the nineteenth.

The fabric of modern industrial Scotland can be said to have been laid within that period and Stirlingshire was not exempt from the acceleration of technological and economic change which historians have labelled the Industrial Revolution. Indeed with the establishment in 1759 of the Carron Ironworks near Falkirk an important forerunner of industrial activity is closely linked with the county. Not only were other ironworks established in various parts of Stirlingshire, but subsidiary industries also developed. These included nail making at Bannockburn and St. Ninians and coal and limestone mining at Kilsyth and Airth. In a considerable number of parishes therefore, the nature of the economy was undergoing significant change in the period with which this paper is concerned. But the changes in Stirlingshire parishes were not all those associated with heavy industry. In the West of the county, in places such as Campsie and Balfron, the nature of the change was primarily that associated with textiles — linen, calico and cotton. Other textiles — plaids and shawls — were being produced at the same time in the far east of Stirlingshire, in Alva. Changes associated with heavy industries and textiles, however, were occurring concurrently with agricultural improvements especially in drainage and ploughing techniques which made the Carse of Stirling into one of the most fertile farming areas in Scotland. Each of these developments also had an effect on the **115** position of the burgh of Stirling itself. Finlay McKichan (1978 p69) has pointed out that

'in the nineteenth century the numbers of bankers, land surveyors, auctioneers, medical practitioners, grain merchants and many types of tradesmen and shopkeepers grew in proportion much more rapidly than did the general population of the town, and reflected the business brought to Stirling from the surrounding area.'

It is against such a background of change that this consideration of the care of the poor is set. What changes did the administrative practice of poor relief undergo between 1790 and 1845?

WHO ADMINISTERED POOR RELIEF?

One of the distinctive features of the system of poor relief in Scotland was the agents by whom it was administered. Like the English legislation with which it was contemporaneous, the Scottish Acts of 1572 and 1579 also envisaged the operation of poor relief as a duty to be undertaken by the civil authorities. While it maintained that feature in England, in Scotland it had become before the end of the sixteenth century a responsibility of the Established Church, by whom informally it was being exercised in some parishes as a Christian duty. The fact that poor relief was already being offered as 'one of the social obligations of a Christian community' (Mitchison 1974 p63) is undoubtedly part of the explanation for the legalising of this practice in the 1590s. But it has also to be seen as part of 'the social impact of the Reformed Church' (Smout 1969 p72). Implicit in the *Book of Discipline* of 1560, drawn up by John Knox and some other Calvinist Reformers, were not oly plans for a spiritual reformation but also a 'wider vision of a Godly Commonwealth' (Smout ibid) in which the administration of poor relief and education were to be of considerable importance in the creation of a Scottish theocracy. Though the strategy envisaged in the *Book of Discipline* was a national one, the policy was to be carried out primarily by the parish which had been 'the Cinderella of the ecclesiastical institutions of the Middle Ages' (Burleigh 1960 p53).

In terms of the Presbyterian polity which the Reformers had devised, parochial responsibility meant that the care of the poor was entrusted to the Kirk Session, an executive committee of the local congregation consisting of the ordained minister of the parish and an unfixed number of laymen described in the *Book of Discipline* (Dickinson 1949) as 'men of best knowledge in God's word and cleanest life, men faithful and of the most honest conversation that

116 can be found in the Kirk'. A contributor to the *Edinburgh Review* (Monypenny 1834 p431) contended that those who fulfilled these requirements came 'invariably from the most respectable classes'. In Stirlingshire heritors or landowners were often among its members, with the parochial schoolmaster, himself usually an appointment of the Kirk Session, serving as clerk.

In addition to their religious duties the Kirk Session exercised a significant social discipline over both public and private life in the community. This is shown especially well in the description of St. Ninians (Stirling) Kirk Session given in NSA (i.e. New Statistical Account of Scotland, 1845) VIII, 318-9

'From 1653 to 1750 there were from 24 to 30 meetings of Session in the year. The ministers and elders exercised most extensive powers both in passing Acts and in punishing delinquents. Besides licentious persons, drunkards, Sabbath breakers and slanderers they took cognisance of those guilty of theft, prevarication or perjury, of scolding and railing. Severe enactments are made against those that haunt public houses, that do not keep the Kirk and the examinations but idle persons such as vagrants and vagabonds and sturdy beggars and also those that 'resett' them are objects of their highest displeasure.

The elders were exorted to see that worship was maintained in every family, and great attention was paid to those who sought for baptism for their children or admission to the Lord's Table. The education of the young was an object of peculiar care and they seem to have exercised an unlimited authority both over the teacher and his scholars. They appoint the parochial schoolmaster and allot him his salary — they instruct him what he is to teach and fix his hours of teaching, when dis-satisfied call him before them, admonish, reprove or dismiss him at their pleasure.'

The administration of poor relief, therefore, was but one among a variety of other duties undertaken by the Kirk Session. Given the involvement in poor relief of the members of these parochial committees across the county however, it was no doubt not only in Alva that elders on admission to the Kirk Session were enjoined to be 'faithful and active in collecting the funds belonging to the poor and distributing of those funds to the most needful' (Scottish Record Office CH2/10/3, 1799, 1830).

The fact that such work was 'a labour of love' as the minister of Kilsyth described it in OSA (i.e. 'Old' Statistical Account 1790-7) XVIII, 255 may have been contested by some of its administrators as well no doubt as some of its beneficiaries. But that it was 'a great labour too' is shown by the following account for the parish of Balfron (NSA VIII, 300) in the late 1830s where 'besides exercising a minute and daily care over all the paupers on the roll, on the first Monday of every month the minister and Kirk Session met when all the paupers who could attend were expected to make their appearance and personally to receive their monthly allowance. Those who could not appear from ill health were waited upon by some member of the Session and their condition reported. Thus was the case of every individual brought monthly under the view of the whole Session. The effects of this system of watchfulness were abundantly apparent. None were admitted on the roll who were not proper objects of charity. None were continued upon it who did not require relief. The poor were well attended to and contented'

Not in every parish, however, did the Kirk Session meet so frequently, make such thorough investigation of its poor nor such regular distributions of its funds. In Gargunnock for example (OSA XVIII, 114) when an old woman who 'had for many years every appearance of extreme indigence' applied to be admitted to the poor's roll she was at once given four shillings per month as 'no doubt was entertained of her poverty.' But when she died

'on examining her bed clothes one purse (of gold and silver) was found after another till the sum amounted to upwards of £40 Sterling... It is evident that the poor woman had lived in great affluence'

Local administration meant not only the possibility . of some assistance being granted to those recognised by local knowledge to be in need, but in the absence of central control, carried with it also the possibilities for the exercise of petty tyranny in a situation where the Kirk Session was also an agent of social discipline. Isobel Thomson 'who has a monthly allowance from the Poor's Fund and has been observed again in the house of liquor' was threatened with the refusal of admission to the sealing ordinances of baptism and the Lord's Supper by the Kirk Session (Kirk Session Records Gargunnock, 1790). In Campsie (Scottish Record Office CH2/5/2,1810) when one of the recipients of relief gave birth to an illegitimate child she was ordered to be struck off the poor roll at least until further investigation was made of her case.

It should not be assumed that in the exercise of their duties as administrators of the system of poor relief the members of the Kirk Sessions in Scotland acted entirely independently and devoid of any central control. Theoretical supervision by an Act of 1600 was placed in the hands of Presbyteries consisting of ministers and elders from a geographically defined area. As Nicholls (1856 p36) pointed out, however, they

'would naturally have a fellow feeling with the inferior body, each

118 of its members being likewise a member of some of the Kirk Sessions within its boundaries and all necessarily acting under similar influences.'

In practice more active supervision could be exercised by the heritors or landowners especially after judgements in the Court of Session in 1751 and 1752. However, in spite of this theoretical power, to assert that the heritors 'controlled poor relief' (Smout 1964 p218) may be something of an overstatement. While the pattern of landowners' involvement was considerably diverse, the general pattern that emerges from the records of Stirlingshire parishes is of a system administered by the members of the Kirk Session with the landowners' role being that of general oversight of the system. The minister of Strathblane (OSA XVIII, 574-5) provided an assessment of the role of Kirk Session that had more general applicability beyond his own parish

'To their discretion is left the apportioning each person's supply and they keep regular books for the inspection of the heritors.'

Such a system could as easily imply satisfaction with the composition of the Kirk Session as it could apathy or indifference on the part of the heritors. I will refer below, however, to the often changed relationship between the heritor and the Established Church which was a factor of some significance, not least for the operation of poor relief in the period with which this paper is concerned.

In the years immediately preceding the reform of poor relief in Scotland in 1845 statistics collected for the General Assembly Report on the Management of the Poor (British Parliamentary Papers 1839, XX) indicated that just over 80 per cent of those involved in the administration of poor relief were members of Kirk Sessions. In Stirlingshire this proportion at 74 per cent was slightly lower than the Scottish average. Of the 52 agents who were classed as other than members of the Kirk Sessions of the county, the largest number was to be found in Stirling itself with its distinctive Poor's Scheme created in 1780. This operated alongside the provision made by individual Kirk Sessions and the clergy were required to share the exercise of their power with members elected annually from among its voluntary subscribers. As in Stirling so too in four of the other five parishes agents other than representatives of the Kirk Session were involved. It was as a supplement to the ecclesiastical administration and not as a replacement for it. It was only in Denny, however, because of a dispute between the heritors and the Kirk Session, that complete control was exercised by a group other than the Kirk Session.

Much more usual at the end of the period with which this paper is concerned, just as at its beginning, was the situation described by a

minister of the Church of Scotland in the early nineteenth century. **119**
For the Rev. Robert Burns the Kirk Session was 'equally despotic in
the affairs of the poor as the Czar of all the Russias' (Scottish
Record Office CH1/2/184, 1841).

WHERE DID THE FUNDS COME FROM?

Since the main agents responsible for the administration of poor
relief were the Kirk Sessions it is hardly surprising that one of the
main sources of revenue for the scheme came from church collections
and other specifically ecclesiastical fees. They were part of a system
(British Parliamentary Papers 1839, XX)
'the object of which is to provide the necessary supplies for the
poor (by placing) its main reliance on the voluntary contributions
of the public and never imposes a compulsory assessment so long
as hopes can be reasonably entertained of procuring without it the
needful assistance.'
Assessment — or a regular tax — for the relief of the poor in
Scotland according to Nicholls (1856 p106) formed 'an exception
instead of being the rule as in England'. That this was so, in spite of
the fact that discretionary rating powers were in existence, was
attributed by Alison (1840 p22), one of the main protagonists in the
campaign to reform the Scottish poor laws in the 1840s, to the fact
that
'the general impression and belief amongst the most influential
persons who have presided over the public charities of Scotland
(is) that all legal provision for the poor is a great evil ... The fear
of weakening the prudence and foresight of the poor by teaching
them to rely on legal relief has been probably not the sole motive
but certainly the most ostensible plea of the characteristic
distinction of the system established in Scotland for the
maintenance of the poor.'
The 1839 General Assembly Report (British Parliamentary Papers
1839, XX, 8) expressed what it saw as the benefits of a system of
voluntary contributions rather than a reliance on regular rating
'the poor are led to be industrious and provident; their relatives
· and neighbours are encouraged to assist them, a spirit of
independence is cherished ... the burden to the industrious part
of the community is lessened.'
Within the voluntary system church collections formed a source of
revenue for the poor in every parish. But the amount that was
collected was conditional on several factors. Of these, the first was
the provision of public worship which required the services of a

120 trained clergyman. Between his death or removal to another parish the congregation was 'vacant' and dependent on the supply of visiting clergy. In Alva for example, between the death of one minister on March 27 1808 and the induction of his successor in April 1809 there were 31 Sundays, or almost half the period in question, on which there was no sermon and from the Treasurer's Account Book for the period (Scottish Record Office CH2/10/6, 1808-9) no collection for the poor. This occurred at times other than the death of a minister or his translation to another parish. In 1796 in the same parish (ibid) 'the minister from home' accounted for ten Sundays and included his attendance at the meetings of the General Assembly in Edinburgh, the Synod of Perth and Stirling, and his assistance at the observation of the Sacrament in neighbouring parishes.

Church collections were also dependent on whether an assessment had been levied in the parish. In Balfron, where from 1831 an assessment had been levied on every individual whose earnings were supposed to be in excess of ten shillings a week, the minister (NSA VIII, 301) drew attention to its effect on church collections

'The springs of charity are dried up, in consequence the collections at the church door are, we may say, almost nothing.'

Two further factors need to be taken into account in considering the amount collected for the poor. First of these is the residence or non residence of the landed proprietors of a parish. The custom of heritors spending increasing periods away from their estates in either Edinburgh or London or their increasing allegiance to the Episcopal Church after the repeal of the penal laws in 1792, all removed from the parish those best able to contribute to the parochial poor fund. 'Your want of funds' the Kirk Session of Campsie was informed in 1823 (Scottish Record Office CH2/51/3, 1823) 'is entirely owing to the non resident heritors not making payment of their subscriptions.' In nearby Kilsyth, 'where most of the heritors do not reside', the minister stated (OSA XVIII, 257) that the sums collected for the poor 'have been collected literally from the poor or from the lower orders of the people.' In the person of George Moir of Leckie, however, who in 1788 donated the sum of 100 guineas to the Poor's Fund of the parish, the Kirk Session of Gargunnock had what their minister considered a model worthy of emulation (OSA XVIII, 113)

'Being of the Scotch Episcopal Communion he seldom attended the Established Church. He saw, however, and had the humanity to acknowledge that the poor of the parish suffered a loss by his absence and when he gave the sum . . . he said he was only paying what he owed them.'

The final factor which conditioned the amount given in the church collections was the extent of Dissent from the Established Church

'The first occasion of the Church collections proving permanently **121**
inadequate in any parish for the maintenance of the ordinary poor
was the rise and progress of Presbyterian secession from the
Established Church' (British Parliamentary Papers 1818, V).
Not without its relevance to Stirlingshire, since Ebeneezer Erskine the
leader of the first such Secession in 1733 had been one of the
ministers of Stirling, the extent of Dissent had obvious implications
to a scheme of relief that relied principally on church door
collections. In at least one Stirlingshire parish according to the
returns made to the Royal Commission on Religious Instruction in
Scotland (Scottish Record Office HH37/60, 1835) those belonging to
other denominations outnumbered those who were members of the
Established Church.

In a situation of this sort what provision for the poor was made
by the Dissenting congregations? In Balfron the minister complained
(NSA VIII, 300) that the Dissenting congregations did not, in spite of
frequent requests, contribute anything to the funds under the
management of the Kirk Session for the relief of the poor though the
poor members of those congregations retained the right to parochial
relief. In Campsie the Rev. James Lapslie expressed the view (OSA
XV, 363) that

'the mode of provision by collections at the Church door has been
considerably hurt by a Relief meeting house which hath lately
been erected in the parish. The collections made at these houses
being employed to pay the debts incurred in building their
chapels, none is given to support the regular poor: such houses,
therefore, upon their present footing are extremely prejudicial to
the Scottish mode of providing for the indigent.'

David Monypenny (1834 p65) usefully summed up the situation in
the mid 1830s

'The Secession constituted one of the causes of a very great
diminution of the collections made at Established Churches while
the burden of this fund is by no means diminished in an equal
proportion by the number of paupers withdrawn from the
Establishment.'

In addition to church door collections, however, there were also
other sources of ecclesiastical revenue available to finance the system
of poor relief. These included the customary dues paid for the
services of the church at birth, marriage and death and by those who
were brought before the Kirk Session in its role as a disciplinary
body. There were also capital sums available to most of the
Stirlingshire parishes. Of these the last three warrant some additonal
discussion.

In the 1820s a practice developed in some of the Stirlingshire

122 parishes of using a hearse without a mortcloth or pall the fee for which had traditionally been an additional revenue to the poor fund (Acts of the Kirk Session of Logie 1829; Kirk Session Records, Polmont 1826, 1835). And in Alva a Burial Society was formed in 1826 whose intention was to procure a mortcloth of their own. This led the Kirk Session to apply for legal opinion and ultimately to secure from the Sheriff an interdict preventing the use of any but the mortcloths owned by the Kirk Session in the parish. It may not be without its significance however, that at a subsequent meeting of the Kirk Session a reduction in the hiring charges for mortcloths was ordered (Scottish Record Office CH2/10/3, 1826). Several other Stirlingshire parishes did likewise at this time (e.g. Scottish Record Office CH2/51/3, 1822, 1829, 1831; Kirk Session Records, Polmont 1826, 1835).

The Kirk Session still remained in the early nineteenth century an agent of social and moral discipline. The most usual penalty for those who incurred its displeasure was that of 'appearing on the stool of repentance and being rebuked from the pulpit' (Graham 1969 p244) in front of the congregation. The wealthier classes however, were often able to escape this public rebuke by payment of a fine and from the end of the eighteenth century fines imposed in lieu of public rebuke became not only a more frequent entry in the Kirk Session records of Stirlingshire but also constituted a significant augmentation of their income (e.g. Scottish Record Office CH2/400/12, 1794; Kirk Session Records Logie 1800; Polmont 1801; Scottish Record Office CH2/51/3, 1815).

Capital sums donated or bequeathed to the parish for its poor, or resulting from the excess of collections over expenditure, constituted one of the main points of difference between parishes in the amount available from accrued interest to be distributed to the poor. The Kirk Session of Alva, for example, had in the 1830s a capital sum of £50 that had been bequeathed to them in 1764 (NSA VIII, 190). The not too distant parish of St. Ninians, by contrast, had accumulated by various bequests a sum in excess of £2000 (NSA VIII, 338-9; Scottish Record Office CH2/337/10, 1833, 1834, 1837). The most common methods of handling such funds used by the Stirlingshire Kirk Sessions were bank deposits or investment in the property or road developments of the period (e.g. NSA VIII, 59; Kirk Session Records Lecropt 1793; Scottish Record Office CH2/479/2, 1813, 1842, 1844; CH2/51/3, 1813). In these ways therefore, often involving significant commercial dealings, the Kirk Sessions sought to provide a regular income for discharging their responsibility as managers of the Poor Funds.

Emphasis has been laid upon the continuing importance of

specifically ecclesiastical sources of revenue for the provision of poor relief. But the pattern in Stirlingshire, as in many other parts of Scotland in the period with which this paper is concerned, was one in which new sources developed alongside the traditional methods.

Nationally by 1839 legal assessments for the relief of the poor were levied in one third of Scottish parishes which tended to be concentrated in the South East, Lanarkshire, South Dumfries and the large towns. Much of the increase in the total funds available for the poor by the time of the General Assembly's Report in 1839 was to be explained by the increase in the amount raised by legal assessment. By that date in fact, almost one half of the total revenue for the poor came from such sources.

Much more common in the changing patterns of raising revenue in Stirlingshire was the development of what were known as voluntary assessments. They represented an intermediate category between the purely voluntary system on the one hand and a statutorily raised rate for the poor on the other. Their basis was a voluntary collection made by the heritors without legal sanctions against those who declined to pay. 'The heritors' as the minister of Fintry expressed it 'assessed themselves voluntarily in a small sum according to circumstances' (NSA VIII, 47). Such voluntary assessments, in the context of the traditional Scottish system, possessed the advantage noted by a contributor to the *Edinburgh Review* (1834 p435) that, 'the poor are not so much disposed to regard it as a certain resource and that it is consequently easier got rid of when the pressure has subsided' Levitt and Smout (1979 p210) have shown in their analysis of returns made to the Poor Law Commission Inquiry in 1843 that such a method of raising revenue for the poor was in operation in up to 60 per cent of the Stirlingshire parishes. In each of the parishes where some form of assessment had been introduced between the time of the Old and New Statistical Accounts (i.e. 1790 and 1845) — Balfron, Campsie, Denny, Fintry, Kilsyth, Kippen and Muiravonside — there had also developed some form of industrial activity. Principally, in the parishes referred to, this was in textiles; but in Muiravonside, where the main employment was in agriculture, the minister also referred to the recent settlement of some 25 families of colliers and 'an unusually large proportion of masons' (NSA VIII, 212). It was to be for the industrial poor 'thrown suddenly idle by depression of trade' (Cockburn 1874 II p2) that the inadequacies of the existing — primarily voluntary — system were to be shown by Alison and his supporters in the campaign for reform in the 1840s.

WHO WERE THE POOR?
HOW WERE THEY RELIEVED?

The emphasis so far in this paper has been upon the administrators of the system and the sources from which they raised their funds. But in considering the operation of the system of poor relief it is also necessary to refer to those who were entitled to receive relief and to the ways in which they might be assisted.

Fundamental to the Scottish system was the denial of the right to relief to the able bodied unemployed. That 'no legal recognition was given to the right of the able bodied to support' (Macdonald 1937 p103) was an inevitable consequence of fifteenth and sixteenth century legislation based on the duty of every citizen to work. But even the reforming legislation of 1845 'was vitiated', according to one assessment (Mitchison 1970 p388) 'by the old Scottish principle that the only qualification for relief must be disability added to destitution'.

Regular relief, paid usually weekly, monthly or quarterly, was to be provided only for those permanently 'disabled from procuring a living by their own labour either by old age or by some permanent bodily infirmity or mental incapacity and who have neither separate means nor any relative who are bound and able to support them' (*Edinburgh Review* 1834 p428).

But in the majority of parishes a further class — that of the occasional poor — was also recognised. Since the final decade of the seventeenth century the authorities responsible for poor relief in Scotland had been permitted to set aside one half of the Church door collections to benefit those experiencing some particular but temporary and exceptional misfortune. The records of the Stirlingshire Kirk Sessions refer to a considerable number of disbursements of this sort, usually denoted by the recipient's name and with the reason for the relief appended. In Gargunnock (Kirk Session Records Gargunnock, 1790) occasional relief of five shillings per month was given to two sisters 'who are at present in very poor circumstances not having received their usual remittance from the West Indies'. Nearly 50 years later in the same parish (ibid 1837) a sum was given to a woman whose husband had recently died 'leaving her in embarrassed circumstances'. An ability to respond to sudden emergencies in the form of occasional relief can be said to have been one of the chief advantages of a system of local management, and it is interesting that the Poor's Fund of the parish of Stirling was criticised in the OSA (VIII, 289-90) because its officers met too seldom 'to give incidental aid, the most useful and necessary of all charity'. Entitlement to occasional relief however, was not — as in the case of the regular poor — a legal right but 'at the discretion of **125** the Kirk Session during the pressure of want'.

It is not surprising therefore, that there was considerable inter parochial variation in the numbers of occasional poor recorded in both the 1818 and 1839 General Assembly Reports. More interesting however, are the relative proportions of regular and occasional poor referred to in those Reports. In 1818 the occasional poor constituted two-thirds of the total number of those in receipt of poor relief in Stirlingshire. By 1839 the number of occasional poor was almost identical to what it had been twenty years earlier but as a proportion of the total number receiving relief, the occasional poor had declined to just over one third. Within a twenty year period, both nationally and locally in Stirlingshire therefore, the trend was away from the pattern of occasional relief to that of permanent allowance. The General Assembly Report sought to explain the increase in the number of regular poor by reference to the fact that the figures for 1839 included dependants. But it is perhaps also possible to see in the increase the result of the practice in parishes in rural areas 'of .giving little or nothing to their own legitimate paupers and rigidly keeping out those from other parishes' (Alison 1840 p6) which tended to cause migration to the more generous and usually assessed urban areas which by 1844 had nearly half of all those in receipt of relief (Levitt and Smout 1979 p175).

Entitlement to relief in Scotland did not only depend on the criteria defining the regular or occasional poor: the responsibility of the parish to provide relief applied to those who had a settlement there, determined either by birth or by three years continuous residence. There is evidence of considerable inter-parochial migration and its effect on the system of poor relief in the records of the Stirlingshire Kirk Sessions from at least the 1820s. Prior to removal back to the parish of origin of an individual claiming relief who had not fulfilled the terms of settlement in the parish from which he was claiming, the Kirk Session generally made enquiries about the individual's legal settlement and of the willingness or otherwise of the poor relief authorities in that parish to defray the expenses that might be incurred in granting relief (e.g. Scottish Record Office CH2/51/3 and 4, 1815, 1820, 1822, 1844; CH2/479/2, 1843; CH2/400/13, 1820). Such a system not only began to generate considerable investigation and correspondence but had led, by the beginning of the 1840s from those in the towns, to pressure for a longer period of settlement and a formal law of removal.

The extent to which the able bodied unemployed may have been relieved as occasional poor in the period with which this paper is concerned is difficult to estimate, not least as Levitt and Smout have

126 recently pointed out (1979 p175) because of the different criteria being used by parish authorities to distinguish between regular and occasional poor. Nor is it possible from the documentary material available in the Kirk Session records to give accurate numbers of those who may have been receiving occasional relief at a time of unemployment since the reason given in the list could well describe some other temporary misfortune such as sickness. On the basis of data from the Poor Law Commission Report of 1844 however, Levitt and Smout (ibid p207) have suggested that up to 20 per cent of Stirlingshire parishes were relieving able bodied men from the poor law. And in the records of two parishes in the county there is also evidence of special measures being introduced by the Kirk Session at a time of trade depression. In Kilsyth in the 1820s when the handloom weaving — on which the parish relied — was significantly declining, the Kirk Session decided that the collections were to be used in aid of the fund established for the relief of unemployed operatives; and in Campsie at the same time the Kirk Session provided outdoor labour for all who were able and willing to work, in what appears to have been an early form of public works scheme (Scottish Record Office CH2/216/6, 1826; CH2/51/3, 1826).

These schemes however, are somewhat outside the usual methods by which the Kirk Sessions sought to provide assistance to those on their poor roll. In a system that was predominantly non-institutional, the main methods of making provision for the poor were by the grant of money and of relief in kind. The total of money available to the Kirk Sessions for distribution was one among several factors that determined the amount of relief that any individual might be paid. The Royal Commission of 1844 (British Parliamentary Papers 1844, XX, xv) concluded that in many parishes

'the quantum of relief given is not measured by the necessities of the pauper but by the sum which the Kirk Session may happen to have in hand for distribution.'

But to such economic considerations was added the moral judgement of the Kirk Session. According to the 1818 General Assembly Report (British Parliamentary Papers 1818, V, 33)

'the consideration of the character and known habits of a pauper has influence with Sessions in regulating the quantum and the kind of allowance bestowed on the respective applicants.'

A third determinant of the amount given as relief was the conception of poor relief as a supplement to what it was expected the poor would have available from other sources. 'The English system is to support the poor' the Rev. James Lapslie of Campsie affirmed (OSA XV, 363), the Scottish to assist them

'It was assumed that family obligations would be fulfilled; that the industrious would be able to save against sickness and old age; that the meagre monetary grants would be supplemented by personal services and private help; that the treatment of the poor would recognise them as persons and that their circumstances would be known to those whom they trusted as their spiritual guides; that they would continue to live with their relatives or in the neighbourhood where they were known' (Saunders 1950 p199)

There is certainly evidence within the period of this study of attempts by the Kirk Sessions of Stirlingshire parishes to re-assert the pattern of family responsibility especially of children caring for their aged parents (e.g. Scottish Record Office CH2/51/4, 1841; CH2/216/5, 1790; also OSA XV, 363; British Parliamentary Papers 1844, XXII, 830). But it has been pointed out by Coats (1973 p6)

'this simple social system could not survive the growth of efficient large scale commercialised agriculture in the eighteenth century, and it was even more helpless in the rapidly expanding urban communities of Glasgow and Edinburgh.'

It is not surprising, therefore, that the amount paid to the poor in Scotland — in contrast with other countries — was to play an important part in Alison's proposals for a revised system of poor relief in the 1840s. At the time only the almost completely assessed area of South East Scotland approximated to the £3 to £4 which those who allied themselves with Alison considered necessary for adequate maintenance. In Stirlingshire, on the basis of the figures presented to the 1839 General Assembly Report, the average amount of relief paid to all the poor was approximately £1 16 shillings per year. That figure however, conceals the very important differences in the amounts being paid to the regular and occasional poor. Payment to the former in the Stirlingshire parishes at £2 10 shillings was some 12 shillings above the Scottish average. Payments to the occasional poor, which averaged approximately 10 shillings, were however, almost one third less than the Scottish average.

The details of money allowances however, do not tell the whole story about the method of maintaining the poor in Scotland in the period before reform. In Fintry for example (OSA XV, 378), 'besides the stated distribution, attention is paid to clothing the most destitute and supplying them with fuel'. In Strathblane (ibid XVIII, 574)

'In addition to their allowance the regular poor were supplied with coals in the winter and for some of them their house rent is paid.'

During the winter at Bothkennar (NSA VIII, 204) there was in addition to the weekly allowance 'an occasional supply of coals and clothing'; while in Drymen (ibid p114) where the distribution of money relief was quarterly, the poor received in addition, 'coals,

128 cordials and extra help when in sickness or destitution'. The payment of fees for medical attendance and the education of orphans and the children of poor parents were also forms of relief in kind for which the Kirk Session bore a financial and social responsibility (e.g. OSA VIII, 278-9; Extracts from the Logie Parish Minutes 1795, 1803; Parish of Logie Cash Book 1832-6; Scottish Record Office CH2/51/3, 1833). So too were the boarding out of orphan children and the care of the elderly without dependants (Scottish Record Office CH2/51/4, 1842; Kirk Session Records Gargunnock 1833). In this respect therefore, the system of poor relief developed not only as a (usually part) provider of financial resources but also as a local agent concerned with a wider range of welfare services.

IN CONCLUSION

I have tried within this paper to provide some indication of the principles and practice of poor relief in Stirlingshire in the period between 1790 and 1845. The theme has principally been one of considerable local administrative continuity. But it cannot be considered in isolation from the broader social, economic, demographic, political and religious changes of the period, each of which, in their own way, created the pressure for national reform and determined the revised administrative structure that was created. Writing of legal assessments in his contribution to the New Statistical Account (VIII, 200) the minister of Polmont reflected

'I trust the day is yet distant when such a mode of providing for their (the poor's) wants must be resorted to because of the manifold evils which it brings in its train.'

That day, in fact, was to be nearer than he thought.

ACKNOWLEDGEMENTS

This paper is based upon my University of Stirling unpublished M.Litt thesis (1973) *The Administration and Reform of Poor Relief in Scotland 1790-1850 with especial reference to Stirlingshire*. I am grateful to my supervisor Professor R. H. Campbell, the staff of the Scottish Record Office and the National Library of Scotland as well as the ministers and Kirk Sessions of Stirlingshire parishes who, at the time of my research, held their records locally.

ALISON, W.P. 1840. On the Management of the Poor in Scotland and its Effect on the Health of Great Towns. Edinburgh.

BRITISH PARLIAMENTARY PAPERS 1818. volume V. Third Report from the Select Committee on the Poor Laws with an Appendix containing Returns from the General Assembly of the Church of Scotland.

BRITISH PARLIAMENTARY PAPERS 1839. volume XX. Report by a Committee of the General Assembly on the Management of the Poor in Scotland.

BRITISH PARLIAMENTARY PAPERS 1844. volumes XX-XXII. Report from Her Majesty's Commissioners for Inquiring into the Administration and Practical Operation of the Poor Laws in Scotland.

BURLEIGH, J.H.S. 1960. A Church History of Scotland. Oxford University Press.

COATS, A.W. editor. 1973. Poverty in the Victorian Age. volume IV. Gregg International.

COCKBURN, HENRY. 1874. Journals. Edmonston and Douglas, Edinburgh.

DICKINSON, W. CROFT editor. 1949. John Knox's History of the Reformation in Scotland. Nelson.

GRAHAM, HENRY GRAY. 1969. The Social Life of Scotland in the Eighteenth Century. 5th edition. A. and C. Black.

KIRK SESSION RECORDS: GARGUNNOCK, LECROPT, LOGIE, POLMONT.

LEVITT, IAN and SMOUT, CHRISTOPHER, 1979. The State of the Scottish Working Class in 1843. Scottish Academic Press, Edinburgh.

MACDONALD, D.F. 1937. Scotland's Shifting Population, 1770-1850. Jackson, Glasgow.

McKICHAN, FINLAY. 1978. A burgh's response to the problems of urban growth: Stirling 1780-1880. *Scottish Historical Review* LVII no. 1, 68-86.

MITCHISON, ROSALIND. 1970. A History of Scotland. Methuen.

MITCHISON, ROSALIND. 1974. The making of the Old Scottish Poor Law. *Past and Present* 63, 58-93.

MONYPENNY on the Scottish Poor Laws, 1834. *Edinburgh Review* LIX, 425-438.

MONYPENNY, DAVID. 1833. Remarks on the Poor Laws and on the Method of Providing for the Poor in Scotland. Edinburgh.

NSA — NEW STATISTICAL ACCOUNT OF SCOTLAND. 1845. Blackwood, Edinburgh.

NICHOLLS, GEORGE. 1856. A History of the Scotch Poor Laws. 1967 edition. Augustus M. Kelly, New York.

OSA — 'OLD' STATISTICAL ACCOUNT OF SCOTLAND. 1790-7. Edinburgh.

SAUNDERS, LAURANCE J. 1950. Scottish Democracy. Oliver and Boyd, Edinburgh.

SCOTTISH RECORD OFFICE
  CH1/2/184. Church of Scotland General Assembly Papers, 1841.
  CH2/10/3. Records of the Kirk Session of Alva.
  CH2/10/6. Accounts of the Parish of Alva.
  CH2/51/2,3,4. Kirk Session Records, Campsie.
  CH2/216/5,6. Kirk Sesson Records, Kilsyth.
  CH2/337/10. Kirk Session Records, St Ninians.
  CH2/400/12,13,14. Minutes of the Acts and Proceedings of the Session of Falkirk.
  CH2/479/2. Minutes of Baldernock Kirk Session and Cash Book.

130

HH37/60. Royal Commission on Religious Instruction in Scotland, 1835. Returns from Stirlingshire.

SMOUT, T.C. 1964. Scottish landowners and economic growth, 1650-1850. *Scottish Journal of Political Economy* XI, 218-34.

SMOUT, T.C. 1969. A History of the Scottish People, 1560-1830. Collins.

AUTHORS' ADDRESSES

Iain Bain, Geographical Magazine, 1 Kensington Gore, London S.W.7

S. J. Harrison, Environmental Science, University of Stirling

Peter S. Maitland, Kenneth East and Kenneth H. Morris, Institute of Terrestrial Ecology, Edinburgh

C. J. Henty, Department of Psychology, University of Stirling

James K. Campbell, 16 W. Newington Place, Edinburgh

John D. Williams, Dumfries and Galloway College of Technology, Dumfries

Andrew Bain, 22 Clarendon Road, Linlithgow

William B. Maclaren, Bothkennar Manse, Falkirk

D. E. Gladstone, Department of Sociology, University of Essex